THIS BOOK BELONGS TO:

_____

_____

_____

_____

_____

Liebe Sammler und Freunde der M.I.Hummel Figuren,

wir sind stolz, Ihnen den ersten kompletten M.I.Hummel Sammler-katalog zu präsentieren, den die Mitarbeiter des Hauses Goebel mit viel Fleiß und in liebevoller Detailarbeit für Sie zusammengestellt haben. Die darin enthaltenen Informationen werden Sie hoffentlich unterstützen, Antworten auf Ihre Fragen zu finden.

Das Familienunternehmen Goebel kann im Jahre 2001 nicht nur auf eine 130-jährige erfolgreiche Firmengeschichte zurückblicken, sondern auch auf ein 25-jähriges Bestehen des M.I.Hummel Clubs. Sie, liebe Sammlerinnen und Sammler, haben mit Ihrer zum Teil jahrezehntelangen Liebe und Treue zu unseren M.I.Hummel Figuren, aber auch mit Ihrer Kritik und Ihren hilfreichen Anregungen ganz erheblich dazu beigetragen.

Die Gesellschafter der W. Goebel Porzellanfabrik GmbH & Co. KG in der 5. und 6. Generation danken Ihnen herzlich für Ihre enge Verbundenheit zu unserem Familienunternehmen. Ihr Zuspruch bedeutet für uns die Verpflichtung, Ihnen auch in Zukunft mit den Produkten unseres Hauses Freude zu bereiten. Dieser Katalog soll dabei den Anfang machen.

Viel Freude beim Lesen wünschen Ihnen

Dear Collectors and Friends of M.I.Hummel Figurines,

We are proud to present you the first complete M.I.Hummel Collector's Catalogue. Our Goebel colleagues have industrially prepared it for you with great attention to detail. The information contained therein will hopefully help you to find answers to your questions.

In the year 2001, the family company of Goebel will look back not only on its successful 130-year history as a company, but also on 25 years of the M.I.Hummel Club. You, dear collectors, have contributed most significantly to this history through your love and loyalty to our M.I.Hummel figurines, some of which has extended over several decades, as well as through your constructive criticism and helpful suggestions.

The partners of the W. Goebel Porzellafabrik GmbH & Co. KG, in the 5th and 6th generations, thank you sincerely for your strong attachment to our family company. For us, your encouragement means the obligation to bring you joy, also in the future, through the products of our company. This catalogue is another step. We hope you enjoy reading it.

Sincerely,

Wilhelm Goebel

Christian Goebel

Detlev Stocke

Ulrich Stocke

1935 – 2000 · 65 Jahre M.J.Hummel Figuren

Das Millennium Jahr 2000 war ein Jahr der Geburtstage und Jubiläen. Auch die W. Goebel Porzellanfabrik konnte einen Geburtstag feiern: Die *M.I. Hummel* Figur wurde 65 Jahre! Die weltbekannten und beliebten Produkte werden wie eh und je in Rödental hergestellt, sind zeitlos und vor allen Dingen von bleibendem Wert. Sie stehen nach wie vor als Wertsymbole für Millionen von Figurenliebhabern in der ganzen Welt. Das Prädikat „Made in Germany" gibt dem Sammler die Sicherheit für die Werktreue. Noch heute werden die Produkte in enger Zusammenarbeit mit der Arbeitsgruppe Hummel im Kloster Sießen nach den Vorlagen von Sr. Maria Innocentia Hummel entwickelt.

In den 65 Jahren seit Markteinführung auf der Leipziger Messe im Jahr 1935 gab es viele technische Veränderungen. Der Produktionsablauf bei der Fertigung von *M.I. Hummel* Produkten hat sich jedoch niemals geändert. Damals wie heute wird jede Figur in reiner Handarbeit gefertigt.

Im Laufe der vielen Jahrzehnte entstanden einige Unikate, die von der Arbeitsgruppe Hummel im Kloster Sießen aus verschiedenen Gründen nicht genehmigt wurden. Diese Prototypen lagern in den Archiven von Goebel oder dem Kloster in Sießen und sind in unserem neuen Sammlerkatalog erstmalig in Farbe abgebildet.

Aufgrund des technischen Fortschrittes, Änderung der verwendeten Rohstoffe und Materialien entstanden Figuren mit geringen Farbabweichungen. Selbst zu Lebzeiten von Sr. Maria Innocentia Hummel wurde an verschiedenen Farbvariationen gearbeitet, um die endgültige Fertigungstecknik festzulegen. Solche Stücke gelten heute als besonders wertvoll. Die in unserem Katalog abgebildeten Figuren zeigen die aktuelle Version.

Durch die erforderlichen Neumodellierungen einzelner Figuren gibt es bei einigen Modellen geringe Größenabweichungen. Die genannten Größenangaben beziehen sich auf die heutige Produktion.

Einige Figuren befinden sich weder in den Archiven von Goebel noch des Klosters. Deshalb konnten wir diese Figuren nicht abbilden. Vielleicht sind Sie der glückliche Besitzer einer solchen Rarität. Wir würden uns freuen, wenn Sie uns für Dokumentationszwecke ein Bild Ihres wertvollen Stückes zusenden könnten.

1935 – 2000 · 65 years of M.J.Hummel Figurines

The millennium year 2000 was a year full of birthdays and anniversaries. Also the W. Goebel Porzellanfabrik is in a festive mood: the *M.I. Hummel* figurines celebrate their 65th birthday! These world-famous and popular products are still being made in Rödental. They are timeless and above all they keep their value. As ever, they are valuable items to millions of collectors all over the world. The title "Made in Germany" is guarantee of origin for the collectors. Today, the products are created in close cooperation with the Hummel board in the Convent of Siessen, according to the drawings of Sister Maria Innocentia Hummel.

Since the 65 years since the first introduction at the Leipzig Trade Fair in 1935, a lot of technical changes were made. The production process of the *M.I.Hummel* products, however, never changed. As always, each figurine is made by hand.

Over the years, unique pieces were created. For several reasons they were not approved by the Hummel board of the Convent. These prototypes are being kept in the Goebel archives or at the Convent of Siessen and for the first time they are listed in color in our new Collector's Catalogue.

Because of technical progress and other new raw materials, there exist figurines with minimal differences in color. Even during the lifetime of Sister Maria Innocentia Hummel, different colors were developed to be able to determine the final production techniques. Today, such pieces are considered to be very valuable. The figurines pictured in our catalogue are the current ones.

Due to necessary resculpting of individual pieces, figurines can be found in different sizes. The sizes mentioned are those of the current production.

Some figurines are not in the possession of Goebel or the Convent; therefore we could not show these figurines. Maybe you are the lucky owner of such a rarity. We would be very pleased if you could send us a picture of your figurine, for documentation purposes.

Inhaltsverzeichnis	Seite	Table of Content	Page
W. Goebel Porzellanfabrik Über 130 Jahre Figuren-Tradition Informationszentrum in Rödental	4 - 5	W. Goebel Porzellanfabrik 130 Years - A Creative Heritage Information Center in Rödental	4 - 5
Maria Innocentia Hummel Das Vermächtnis einer Künstlerin	6 - 7	Maria Innocentia Hummel An Artist's Legacy	6 - 7
M.I.Hummel Figuren Handarbeit von Anfang an	8 - 11	M.I.Hummel Figurines Craftsmanship from the start	8 - 11
Echtheitsmerkmale, Bodenmarken	12 - 14	Marks of Authenticity, Trademarks	12 - 14
M.I.Hummel Club	15 - 17	M.I.Hummel Club	15 - 17
Figurenkollektion	18 - 256	Figurines	18 - 256
M.I.Hummel Miniaturen	257 - 258	M.I.Hummel Miniatures	257 - 258
M.I.Hummel Puppen	259 - 263	M.I.Hummel Dolls	259 - 263
Index	264	Index	264

Goebel®

W. Goebel Porzellanfabrik
Germany

Goebel of North America L.L.C.
Goebel Plaza
Route 31
P.O. Box 10
Pennington, NJ 08534-0010
USA
Tel.: (800) 666-2582 · Fax: (800) 486-6354
Internet: www.mihummel.com

N.C. Cameron & Sons, Limited
Ontario, Canada
Tel.: (905) 673-9200 or (800) 263-7095

GOEBEL
Über 130 Jahre Figuren-Tradition

Mit Weitblick planen, Ungewohntes beginnen, Bewährtes übernehmen, Neues wagen – das ist die Kunst des Unternehmers seit alters her. Nach diesen Grundsätzen vollzog sich die Entwicklung unseres Hauses konsequent, harmonisch und seit mehr als 100 Jahren. Denn mehr als ein Jahrhundert ist es her, dass Franz Detleff Goebel mit seinem Sohn William am 30. Januar 1871 die Firma F. & W. Goebel gründete. Dieser am Fuße der Veste Coburg gelegene Betrieb wurde zum Grundstein eines natürlich gewachsenen Unternehmens, das heute Weltgeltung besitzt. Zunächst wurden dort Schiefertafel, Griffel und Märbel produziert. Dann – als hätte man schon damals modernes Marketing-Denken gekannt – folgten Gebrauchsgegenstände des täglichen Bedarfs: Milchkrüge, Kannen, Kaffeeservice, Eierbecher und andere Artikel aus Porzellan.

Mit der Fertigung von Porzellanfiguren brach um 1900 eine neue Ära an. Hier wurde der erste Schritt getan, der zur internationalen Bedeutung des Hauses Goebel führte.

Nach dem Tod des Firmengründers im Jahre 1909 widmete sich sein Sohn William mit Elan und Einsatz dem Ausbau des Unternehmens. Ihn lockte der Export, und die bald einsetzende Nachfrage nach Goebel-Erzeugnissen auf den internationalen Märkten gab ihm recht. Eines der größten Absatzgebiete wurden bis zum heutigen Tage die Vereinigten Staaten von Amerika. Wie wichtig dieses Konzept war, zeigte sich auf den Leipziger Messen, wo die Einkäufer Max Louis Goebel bezeichnenderweise den „Neuheiten-Goebel" nannten. (Es versteht sich, dass wir auf diesen Ehrennamen auch heute noch stolz sind.)

Ab 1929 erlebte die Porzellanfabrik grundlegende technische Verbesserungen und eine erhebliche Kapazitätserweiterung. Man begann mit der Produktion von Feinsteingut und figürlicher Kunstkeramik. Im gleichen Jahr stellte Franz Goebel, in enger Zusammenarbeit mit seiner Mutter Frida und seinem Schwager Dr. Eugen Stocke, die Weichen für weitere Jahrzehnte kontinuierlich steigenden Erfolgs.

Die gemütvoll liebenswerten „M.I.Hum-mel"-Figuren, von der Franziskanerin Maria Innocentia Hummel gezeichnet, traten als dreidimensionale Figuren im Jahre 1935 ihren Siegeszug rund um die Erde an. Heute sind die handgefertigten „M.I.Hummel"-Figuren in der ganzen Welt Stolz und Freude einer internationalen Sammlergemeinde.

Das dynamische – und vor allen Dingen organische – Wachsen wurde selbst durch Kriegs- und Nachkriegszeit kaum gestört.

Als Franz Goebel 1969 starb, hinterließ er eine wohlfundierte Unternehmensgruppe mit Firmen im In- und Ausland. Nach wie vor ist der Leitspruch der 5. und 6. Unternehmergeneration, der Herren Wilhelm und Christian Goebel sowie Ulrich und Detlev Stocke: „Dem Gestern verbunden, dem Heute gewachsen, das Morgen gestaltend."

Die Markenzeichen „Goebel" und „M.I. Hummel" sind nach wie vor im wachsenden Maße Wertsymbole für Millionen von Figurenliebhabern in aller Welt.

More than a century has passed since Franz Detleff Goebel and his son William founded F. & W. Goebel on January 30, 1871. Originally, the company produced slates, slate pencils and toy marbles, but soon it expanded into the production of pitchers, pots, coffee sets and other useful china tableware. The first factory, at the base of Coburg Castle, became the cornerstone of W. Goebel Porzellanfabrik, as the firm is known today.

Through far-sighted planning, exploring new and uncharted avenues, adopting unique methods, and modernizing traditional approaches, the house of Goebel developed rapidly.

The 20th century began a new era, and the F. & W. Goebel Company contributed to it by introducing porcelain figurines. This was the firm's first step in its climb to international fame. When Franz Detleff died in 1909, his son expanded the family enterprise with flair. William concentrated on the export market, and the demand for Goebel products throughout the world proved him astute in doing so. One of the largest markets for the firm has been, and is today, the U.S.A. Max Louis Goebel, William's son, had tremendous creative talent, coupled with a subtle intuition for marketing.

His unique ideas were well received and helped expand the Goebel collections considerably. With the introduction of many unusal items, Max Louis Goebel was nicknamed "Novelty Goebel" at the Leipzig Fairs where he was constantly sought out by buyers. Needless to say, we remain proud of this name today.

Starting in 1929, great strides were made to incorporate technical improvements and expand the production facilities of the company. The manufacture of fine earthenware products, including figurines, began. It was also in 1929 that Franz Goebel, with his mother Frida and his brother-in-law, Dr. Eugen Stocke, began their successful direction of the firm. And, in 1935, the three-dimensional adaptations of Sister M.I. Hummel's sketches were introduced.

Now the charming handcrafted "M.I.Hummel" figurines are cherished proudly by an ever-growing community of devoted collectors throughout the world.

The growth of W. Goebel Porzellanfabrik, ever in wartime and postwar years, was seldom slowed.

When Franz Goebel died in 1969, he left a well-established group of enterprises with subsidiaries and affiliates both in Germany and abroad. After the company's 125th anniversary in 1996, today's motto for the fifth and sixth generation partners, Messrs Wilhelm and Christian Goebel, as well as Ulrich and Detlev Stocke is: „Linked to the past – prepared for today – shaping the future".

The distinctive Trademarks „Goebel" and „M.I.Hummel" continue to be internationally respected symbols of value in the porcelain figurine trade around the world.

Besuchen Sie das Informationszentrum der W. Goebel Porzellanfabrik!

Schauen Sie den Künstlern und Kunsthandwerkern über die Schulter und erleben Sie, wie eine Keramikfigur entsteht.
Lassen Sie sich verzaubern von der einzigartigen Welt der M.I.Hummel-Figuren und der vielen anderen Geschenkartikel aus dem Hause Goebel.

Öffnungszeiten: Montag - Freitag   9 - 17 Uhr
                      Samstag   9 - 12 Uhr

Weitere Informationen erhalten Sie unter 09563/92-303.
Wir freuen uns auf Ihren Besuch!

Visit the Information Center of W. Goebel Porzellanfabrik!

Come and see for yourself how M.I.Hummel figurines are made. Watch over the shoulders of the artists at Goebel and experience "live" the creation of an M.I.Hummel figurine.

Goebel in Rödental welcomes you:
Monday - Friday   9 am - 5 pm
Saturday   9 am - noon

Should you have any questions, feel free to contact us at any time, Phone 09563/92-303. We're looking forward to your visit!

MARIA INNOCENTIA HUMMEL
Das Vermächtnis einer Künstlerin

M.J.Hummel®

Ein Name, den Millionen Menschen in aller Welt kennen: Maria Innocentia Hummel. Ein Name, bei dem man sofort an aufgeweckte Kinder denkt, die ganz in ihr Spiel vertieft sind, sei es nun, dass sie als Erwachsene posieren, mit Freunden herumtollen, geliebte Tiere beobachten oder mit Hingabe die kleinen Arbeiten auf dem Bauernhof verrichten.

Maria Innocentia Hummel gewann Weltruhm als eine in wunderbarer Weise begabte Kindermalerin, deren Skizzen, Zeichnungen und Gemälde durch die kongeniale Interpretation des Künstlerteams bei Goebel die Grundlage der nach ihr benannten Figuren und Relief-Artikel bilden.

Sie wurde als Berta Hummel 1909 in Bayern geboren. Schon im Kindesalter zeigte sich ihr ausgeprägtes schöpferisches Talent. Im Jahre 1927, mit 18 Jahren, vollzog dann das junge Mädchen, das bis dahin meist unter der fürsorglichen Obhut ihrer Eltern gelebt hatte, einen bedeutenden Schritt.

Ihr Vater , dessen eigene künstlerische Neigungen – wenngleich nicht ausgebildet – in ihrer Entwicklung eine bedeutende Rolle gespielt haben mochten, begleitete sie nach München, der bayerischen Landeshauptstadt.

Dort schrieb sie sich als Studentin an der Akademie für Angewandte Kunst ein. Nach vier Jahren hatte sie das akademische Grundstudium, dem sich in späteren Jahren noch ein Aufbaustudium anschloß, beendet. Diese vier Jahre brachten sie nicht nur in ihrer künstlerischen Ausbildung weit voran, so dass ihr die Lehrer dort eine große Zukunft voraussagten, sondern stärkten auch eine weitere Antriebskraft ihres Schaffens.

In ihrem ganzen bisherigen Leben hatte sie aus dem Glauben tiefe Eindrücke empfangen. Das begann in der Kindheit, wo sie in einer überwiegend katholischen Gegend im Kreise der strenggläubigen Familie aufwuchs. Auch in München war das nicht anders. Sie zog aus dem bisherigen Studentenquartier in das Mädchenwohnheim der Familienschwestern. Hier begegneten ihr zwei Franziskanerinnen aus dem Kloster Sießen in Württemberg.

Die beiden Schwestern absolvierten gerade ein Studium, denn das Kloster eines Schulordens legte besonderen Wert auf künstlerisches Schaffen im Bereich der bildenden Kunst. Ihre Freundschaft mit den beiden Ordensschwestern und der Gedanke, Kunst und Religion in ihrem künftigen Schaffen zu verbinden, führten Berta Hummel zu dem Entschluß, ihr Leben fortan im Kloster zu verbringen, abseits von der wachsenden Unruhe im Lande.

Als sie im April 1931 ihr Studium als Klassenbeste abschloß, trat sie, sehr zum Leidwesen ihrer Professoren, ins Kloster ein. Im August 1933 wurde sie eingekleidet und erhielt den Namen Schwester Maria Innocentia. Am 30. August 1934 legte sie ihr Ordensgelübde ab.

Zu ihren vielfältigen Aufgaben gehörte auch der Zeichenunterricht an einer vom Kloster geführten Schule. Aus ihrer großen Liebe zu Kindern erwuchsen jene Zeichnungen von spielenden Kindern – von Freunden aus vergangenen Tagen und jenen, die zum Spielen in den Klostergarten kamen. Jetzt erst fand sie auch zu ihrem eigenen Stil. Eine erste Ausstellung ihrer Werke erregte Aufsehen, und bald stellten sich auch Verleger ein. So lernte Franz Goebel ihre Zeichnungen kennen.

Zusammen mit den Meisterbildhauern Reinhold Unger und Arthur Möller aus seinen Ateliers prüfte er die Möglichkeiten, diesen Zeichnungen in Form von Figuren neues Leben zu verleihen. Schließlich traf er mit der Künstlerin und ihrer Oberin zusammen. Man schloß ein Lizenzabkommen. Es gab der Firma W. Goebel Porzellanfabrik die Alleinherstellungs- und Vertriebsrechte für die dreidimensionale Ausführung nach den Zeichnungen der Künstlerin.

Als Goebel 1935 die ersten Figuren auf der Messe in Leipzig vorstellte, begann die aufregende Geschichte eines großen internationalen Erfolges. Um eine im Lizenzvertrag getroffene Vereinbarung zu erfüllen, die dem Kloster das entscheidende Wort bezüglich künstlerischer Werktreue vorbehielt, besuchte Schwester Maria Innocentia Hummel das Werk. Sie traf sich hier mit den Künstlern, damit die Umwandlung von Bild in plastische Gestalt nach Form und Farbe ganz in ihrem Sinne sei. Das Leben dieser bedeutenden Frau erfüllte sich leider viel zu früh. Im November 1946 fiel sie, erst 37jährig, einer Tuberkulose zum Opfer.

Ihr begnadetes Künstlertum lebt jedoch in wunderbarer Weise in den „M.I.Hummel"-Figuren fort. Deren Herstellung in Handarbeit unterliegt wie ehedem den strengen Prinzipien der Werktreue.

Ein Team aus Künstlern und Mitgliedern des Managements legt einem Sachverständigengremium aus dem Kloster jedes neue Modell in zwei verschiedenen Entwicklungsstufen zur Begutachtung vor.

So sind „M.I.Hummel"-Figuren zu Sinnbildern unbeschwerter Kindertage geworden – Millionen Menschen zur Freude.

Arthur Möller, Franz Goebel und Reinhold Unger im „Cafe am Dom" in München. Hier fiel 1934 die Entscheidung, die Zeichnungen Schwester Hummels in dreidimensionale Figuren umzusetzen.
Arthur Möller, Franz Goebel and Reinhold Unger in "Café am Dom" in Munich. Here, in 1934, the decision was made to transform Sister Hummel's artwork into three-dimensional figurines.

A name known to millions of people the world over: Maria Innocentia Hummel. A name that signifies bright young children thoroughly engrossed in their activities, whether they are playing at being grown-up, doing their farm chores, enjoying time with friends or exploring the ways of amiable animals.

Maria Innocentia Hummel became known to the world as the marvelously gifted artist whose sketches, drawings and paintings have become the inspiration for the three-dimensional and bas-relief renderings of her work created by the superlative team of sculptors, artists and artisans at the Goebel company.

Born Berta Hummel in Bavaria in 1909, it did not take long for her creative talents to become apparent. Even as a child her abilities were evident. When she was eighteen in 1927, a remarkably big step was taken by this young woman who had never been far from home or away from her family.

Berta's father, whose own inclinations toward art, though unrealized, had perhaps played an important role in her artistic development, accompanied her to Munich, the capital of the state of Bavaria. There Berta enrolled at the Munich Academy of Applied Arts, from which she was to graduate four years later.

During those four years, as she made tremendous creative strides and became a student considered by her teachers to have a great artistic future, she also strengthened another force in her life.

Throughout her lifetime, the importance of religion was very strong. Brought up in an area that was predominantly Catholic, Berta and her family were deeply religious. Even in the metropolis of Munich, she shied away from living in accommodations frequented by most students and lived instead in a boarding house run by an order of the church. There she met two sisters of the Franciscan Order from the Convent of Siessen, located in the state of Württemberg, not too far west of Munich and near the Black Forest. The convent, a teaching order then as it is today, placed great emphasis on the arts. The two sisters were in Munich furthering their training. Drawn by this friendship, comforted by the thought of a peaceful convent away from the growing turmoil in Germany, young Berta made her decision.

In April 1931, upon her graduation from the Academy and much to the disappointment of her instructors, she entered the convent. Upon taking her vows she took the name Maria Innocentia. In order to

help raise revenue she received permission to exhibit and sell some of her art.

It wasn't long before her charming postcards depicting children, both those remembered from childhood and those who were now coming into the convent garden to play, came to the attention of Franz Goebel. The fourth-generation owner and head of the company bearing his family name was in search of inspiration for a new line of figurines – and here it was!

With his master sculptors, then Reinhold Unger and Arthur Möller, he explored the possibilities of recreating these two-dimensional representations into three-dimension. He ultimately met with the Mother Superior and with Sister Maria Innocentia. A licence agreement was granted W. Goebel Porzellanfabrik, providing Goebel the sole right to make and distribute three-dimensional adaptations of the artist's work.

Introduced in 1935 at the Leipzig Fair, a major international trade show at the time,

the first figurines were on their way to the tremendous success that has been theirs ever since. To implement the clause in the licensing agreement giving the convent final artistic control, Sister Maria Innocentia even visited the factory herself, meeting the various artists to ensure that the translation from paper to ceramic was as true as possible. Following the strict standards she established during her life-time, the figurines continue to be made by hand. Today, the chief artists involved and the management team journey to the convent, showing each new piece in its various stages of development.

The life of the remarkable woman, Sister Maria Innocentia Hummel, ended much too soon, when she was only 37. In November 1946, succumbing to tuberculosis, Sister Maria Innocentia Hummel died. But her spirit still lives in the shining, exuberant ceramic odes to life, brilliantly transformed into three dimensions for all the world to enjoy.

Schwester Maria Innocentia Hummel (rechts) mit Franz Goebel während eines Besuches des Fabrikanten im Kloster Sießen im Sommer 1936.
Sister Maria Innocentia Hummel (right) with Franz Goebel, during one of his visits to the Convent of Siessen, in summer 1936.

M.I.HUMMEL FIGUREN
Handarbeit von Anfang an

Das Tonmodell

Der erste Schritt bei der Entwicklung einer M.I.Hummel Figur ist das Modellieren.
Bei der W. Goebel Porzellanfabrik wird schwarzer, besonders plastischer und damit gut formbarer und sehr feiner Ton verarbeitet (Bild 1). Er ist einerseits weich wie Knetmasse, dabei doch standfest, schmiegsam mit hervorragenden plastischen Eigenschaften.

Nun beginnt die schwere Aufgabe des Modelleurs, diesem noch unförmigen Klumpen aus Ton, Form und Gestalt zu geben (Bild 2). Nach einer dreijährigen Ausbildung müssen die erfahrenen Modelleure bereits bei dem groben Aufbau des Tonmodelles technische Anforderungen für die spätere kunsthandwerkliche Fertigung berücksichtigen.
Sie müssen auf ein harmonisches Gesamtbild achten und natürlich auf der Grundlage der zeichnerischen Vorlagen von Maria Innocentia Hummel ein dreidimensionales Modell anfertigen, wobei schon jetzt die Größe der späteren Figur festgelegt wird.

Jetzt (Bild 3) beginnt in der nächsten Phase (Bild 4) die feine Ausarbeitung der Figur. Dabei tauscht sich der Modelleur immer wieder mit Kollegen der Formenfertigung, der Gießerei und der Malerei aus, um sicherzustellen, dass die Figur später auch garniert und dekoriert werden kann.

Nach der Fertigstellung der Figur (Bild 5), in diesem Fall „Die Pusteblume" (Hum 475), hat der Modelleur mehrere Wochen Tag für Tag jedes Detail mehrmals überarbeitet.
Für die Ausarbeitung werden neben Modellierwerkzeugen aus Metall auch selbstgestaltete Utensilien aus Holz verwendet, mit Hilfe eines Stechzirkels können Proportionen und Abmessungen genau eingehalten werden.

Nach der Genehmigung des Tonmodelles durch ein Gremium von Sachverständigen des Klosters Siessen kann die Figur in die Modell- und Formenfertigung weitergegeben werden, um die erforderlichen Formen für die Herstellung der Figuren anzufertigen.

Auch die fertig dekorierte Figur wird vor der Serienfertigung nochmals im Kloster vorgestellt, um eine Farbgebung im Sinne von Maria Innocentia Hummel zu gewährleisten.

Fig./Abb. 1

Fig./Abb. 2

Fig./Abb. 3

Fig./Abb. 4

Fig./Abb. 5

The clay model

The first step in developing an M.I. Hummel figurine is sculpting. At the W. Goebel Porzellanfabrik, the sculptors work with very fine, black, highly plastic clay material (Fig. 1). It is as soft as plasticine and supple, but retains its solid, fantastic plastic qualities.

The sculptor has the difficult task to form this lump of clay into a figurine (Fig. 2). Each sculptor is trained in all the needed skills during three years. At the end of a three-year training program, each experienced sculptor keeps the technical requirements of the handwork production that will follow in mind during the modelling phase. Of course, a drawing of Maria Innocentia Hummel always forms the basis for the clay model. The sculptor has to pay attention to the harmonic overall picture and the resemblance with the drawing. The later size of the figurine is now determined.

In the next phase (Fig. 3 and 4), the details are completed. During this process, the sculptor has regular contacts with colleagues from the mould, casting and painting departments to make sure that later on the figurine can be fitted together and painted.

By the time the clay model is ready, Hum 475 "Make A Wish" in this case, the sculptor has reworked every detail several times. This very accurate work takes several weeks.
Besides special metal modelling tools, self-made wooden instruments are also used. With the help of dividers, proportions and measurements are exactly maintained.

After the expert board of the Convent of Siessen has approved the clay model, it is taken to the mould and casting department. All necessary moulds for the production are now made.
When the prototype has been painted, it is taken to the expert board again to assure that the colours correspond with those used in Sister Maria Innocentia Hummel's drawings.

Die Form

Hummel-Figuren können nie aus einem Stück gegossen werden. Je bewegungsvoller und aufgelockerter sie sind, desto größer wird die Anzahl der Einzelteile.

Zunächst wird die Tonfigur zerschnitten, um festzulegen, wieviele abgießbare Teile benötigt werden. Später werden die Einzelteile in der Gießerei wieder paßgenau zusammengesetzt, dass nur noch die Experten wissen, wo die „Nahtlinien" verlaufen.

Für die Herstellung der Gießformen werden zunächst Gipsabdrücke der Einzelteile aus Ton hergestellt (Bild 6). Dazu werden die Stücke behutsam in Ton eingebettet und anschließend mit Gips übergossen. Wenn der Gips abgebunden hat, ist eine Halbform fertig. Sie muß noch nachgeschnitten, geglättet und mit Schlössern, also Kerben und Fixierzapfen, die das Verrutschen der Formenhälften verhindern, versehen werden (Bild 7).
Nun wird von der Rückseite der Einzelteile ebenfalls ein Gipsabdruck abgenommen. So entsteht aus beiden Hälften eine paßgenau schließende Form, deren Hohlraum exakt dem Äußeren des Figurenteiles entspricht. Dieses erste Gießteil wird Mutterform genannt.

Von der negativen Mutterform wird nun ein positiver Abguß aus hochfestem Kunstharz angefertigt, das Arbeitsmodell.
Von dem Arbeitsmodell werden schließlich Arbeitsformen abgenommen, wobei der Prozeß im Prinzip der gleiche wie bei der Herstellung der Mutterform ist.

Die nun vorliegende Arbeitsform ist der Schlüssel des Fertigungsverfahrens und wird in die Gießerei weitergeleitet (Bild 8). Doch kann sie nur für die Herstellung einer begrenzten Zahl von Figuren verwendet werden, weil die flüssige Gießmasse den Gips bei jeder Nutzung auswäscht und die Konturen unscharf werden läßt. Von dem Arbeitsmodell kann aber jederzeit wieder eine neue identische Arbeitsform gegossen werden.

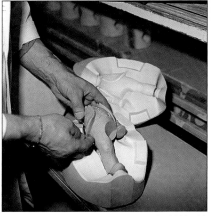

Fig./Abb. 10

Fig./Abb. 9

Fig./Abb. 8

The mould

Hummel figurines can never be cast in one piece. The livelier they are, the more pieces are needed for a figurine.
First the clay model is cut into several pieces, in order to determine how many moulds have to be made. Later on, the individual parts are accurately fitted together in the casting department. Afterwards, only experts can tell where the seams are.

For the production of the moulds, plaster casts are made of the individual parts (Fig. 6). The pieces are embedded in clay and covered with plaster. When the plaster has dried, one half of the mould is ready. This half has to be smoothed out and it gets "locks" (notches, which prevent the moulds from slipping out of place) (Fig. 7). Now the backside of the piece is cast in plaster. These two halves build an accuratly fitting mould. The hollow space inside the mould corresponds exactly with the piece of clay. This very first mould is called the "mother mould".

From the negative mother mould, a positive model of synthetic resin is made. This is the working model.
This working model is used to produce the working moulds. The procedure to make the working moulds is the same as for the mother mould.

The working moulds now go to the casting department (Fig. 8). These moulds can only be used for a limited number of figurines, because the liquid ceramic mass dissolves a bit of the plaster each time the mould is used, and so the details fade away. But with the working model of synthetic resin countless numbers of working moulds can be made.

Gießen und Garnieren

Nach der Herstellung der Arbeitsformen in der Modell- und Formenfertigung, können nun die Einzelteile einer M.I.Hummel Figur gegossen werden.

Dazu wird in der Gießerei die flüssige keramische Masse, der sogenannte Schlicker, der aus Kaolin, Quarz, Feldspat und Wasser zusammengesetzt ist, in die Arbeitsformen aus Gips eingegossen (Bild 9). Die Arbeitsform entzieht nun der Gießmasse die Feuchtigkeit, an den Formenwänden bildet sich nach einiger Zeit der sogenannte „Scherben".

Fig./Abb. 6

Fig./Abb. 7

M.I.HUMMEL FIGUREN
Handarbeit von Anfang an

Fig./Abb. 11

Fig./Abb. 12

Die innere, noch flüssige keramische Masse wird ausgegossen und kann für weitere Figuren wieder aufbereitet werden. Von der Erfahrung des Gießers hängt es ab, wann dies geschehen muß, denn je länger der Schlicker in der Form steht, desto dicker wird der Scherben.

Anschließend werden die beiden Formenhälften geöffnet und der noch weiche Formling vorsichtig herausgelöst (Bild 10).

Beim Garnieren setzen nun geschulte Hände alle Einzelteile zu einer Figur zusammen.
Eine M.I.Hummel Figur kann aus bis zu 40 Einzelteilen bestehen, die sorgfältig und vorsichtig zusammengesetzt werden müssen. Als "Klebstoff" wird wieder die flüssige keramische Masse verwendet.

Nachdem die jetzt vollständig garnierte Figur an der Luft getrocknet ist, wird sie mit Messer und Pinsel verputzt, verwaschen und von Gießnähten befreit (Bild 11).

Jede Figur erhält darüber hinaus ein Luftloch, damit die sich ausdehnende Luft während des Brandes ungehindert aus der hohlen Figur entweichen kann.

Im Anschluß an die Garnierarbeiten erfolgt der erste Brand, der Schrüh- oder Glühbrand bei 1140°C, durch den die keramische Masse ihre Standfestigkeit und Güte erhält. Rund acht Prozent Gewicht verliert die Skulptur im ersten Brand, was sich zugleich auf ihre Größe auswirkt, die sich am Ende um genau dieses Maß verringert hat.

Casting and assembling

In the casting department the individual parts of an M.I.Hummel figurine are made.

The liquid ceramic mass, called slip, is poured into the moulds (Fig. 9). The slip consists of kaolin, quartz, feldspar and water. The mould absorbs the water of the slip and after some time, a shell develops. The longer the slip stays in the mould, the thicker the shell becomes. When the shell has reached the correct thickness, the excess slip is poured out, and can be re-used.

Both halves of the mould are opened and the still wet, soft ceramic piece is carefully removed (Fig. 10).
Experienced hands now assemble the individual parts to a complete figurine. The slip is used as the "glue".
An M.I.Hummel figurine can consist of up to 40 different parts, which must be accurately fitted together.

When the figurine has dried, it is cleaned with a knife and brush. All unevennesses and casting seams are removed (Fig. 11).

Also each figurine receives an air hole, so that the expanding air can escape during the firing.

After the assembling follows the first firing at 1140°C, the biscuit fire. This first firing gives the ceramic mass its stability and the figurine is no longer fragile. The figurine looses about 8 % of its weight during the biscuit fire, therefore it becomes smaller.

Das Malen

Im Anschluß an den Glühbrand erfolgt das Glasieren (Bild 12). Die Glasur, die aus Wasser, Kaolin, Quarz und Feldspat besteht, kann durch Tauchen oder per Spritzpistole auf die Figur aufgebracht werden.

Durch einen zweiten Brand bei 1080° C, dem Glattbrand, wird die Glasur dauerhaft mit dem Scherben verschmolzen. Die aus Kontrollzwecken blau eingefärbte Glasur überzieht nach dem Brand die glänzend weiße Figur mit einem transparenten, panzerartigen Schutz. Die Farbpigmente verbrennen rückstandslos.
Nun kann die Bemalung der Figur erfolgen. Wobei auf eine Farbpalette zurückgegriffen werden kann, die mehrere hundert Farben umfaßt.
Um die noch blassen weißen Figuren „lebendig" erscheinen zu lassen, verwenden jahrelang geschulte Porzellanmaler handgearbeitete Pinsel aus feinsten Haaren und Borsten.

Zunächst werden die Gesichter der M.I.Hummel Figuren ausgezeichnet, d.h. die Augen werden mit der Feder, der Mund, Augenbrauen und Mundhöhlen werden mit kleinsten Pinseln aufgetragen (Bild 13).

Im Anschluß daran wird die Fleischfarbe, die Wangenfarbe und ein leichter Elfenbeinton mittels einer Spritzpistole aufgetragen (Bild 14).

Um die Aufglasurfarbe dauerhaft mit der Glasur zu verschmelzen, muß die Figur eine weitere Brandphase durchlaufen. Dieser Dekorbrand erfolgt bei einer Temperatur von 640°C.

Jetzt erst kann jede einzelne Figur weiter dekoriert werden (Bild 15).
Nachdem versierte Facharbeiter jedes Detail einer Hummel Figur dekoriert haben, wird in einem zweiten Dekorbrand, ebenfalls bei 640°C, die Farbe auf der Figur wieder dauerhaft eingebrannt.

Schließlich wird jede einzelne Figur einer abschließenden Kontrolle unterzogen und kann verpackt werden. Bei jeder Figur finden, über den gesamten Produktionsprozeß verteilt, mehr als 50 Qualitätsprüfungen statt.

The decoration

After the first firing follows glazing (Fig. 12). Immersing or spraying with a spraying pistol applies the glaze, consisting of kaolin, quartz and feldspar.

During the glaze firing at 1080° C, the glaze fuses with the ceramic shell of the

Fig./Abb. 13

Fig./Abb. 14

figurine. The initially blue glaze becomes white during the firing (for controll purposes). All colour pigments are burned out.

After the glaze firing, the figurine can be painted. Several hundreds of colours have been developed for the M.I.Hummel figurines. To give life to the pale, white figurines, the skilled painters use hand-made brushes with the finest hair and bristles.
First the faces of the M.I.Hummel figurines are painted. The eyes are drawn with a pen, the mouth and eyebrows with the finest brushes (Fig 13).

After that, the skin colour, blush and an ivory colour are applied with an air-brush (Fig. 14).

To make the painting permanent, the figurine has to be fired again. At 640° C, the decoration firing permanently melts the colours into the glaze.

Only now, can other colours be applied. After skilled painters have painted all details of the Hummel figurine, it receives a second decoration firing at 640° C, during which the colours are once again permanently melted into the glaze.

Finally, each figurine can be checked and packed. A figurine passes more then 50 quality checks in its course of production.

Fig./Abb. 15

Sammler und Bewunderer aus der ganzen Welt sind sich einig, dass die künstlerische Vollendung und die Qualität eines M.I. Hummel-Produktes einmalig in der Welt sind. Es ist wichtig zu wissen, dass nur echte M.I.Hummel-Figuren gemäß strengster Qualitätskontrollen hergestellt werden. Dies wurde in den 30er Jahren zwischen Schwester Maria Innocentia Hummel und Goebel vereinbart.

Um erkennen zu können, ob eine Figur, ein Teller oder eine Glocke ein authentisches M.I.Hummel-Produkt von Goebel ist, gibt es zwei maßgebliche Identifikationsmerkmale. Das erste ist das offizielle Goebel Markenzeichen. Obwohl sich das Aussehen des Zeichens seit 1935 mehrmals geändert hat, trägt jede echte M.I.Hummel-Figur auf ihrer Unterseite einen Goebelstempel. Ist dieser Stempel nicht sichtbar, kann es sich nicht um eine echte M.I.Hummel-Figur handeln.

Das andere maßgebliche Merkmal ist die Unterschrift von Schwester Maria Innocentia Hummel auf jedem Hummel-Produkt von Goebel. Als Schwester Hummel ihren historischen Vertrag mit Franz Goebel abschloß, wurde vereinbart, dass ihre Unterschrift – das persönliche Siegel ihres Einverständnisses – auf jedem Stück erscheinen sollte. Diese Vereinbarung gilt heute noch.

Wenn Sie sich für ein M.I.Hummel-Produkt entscheiden, kaufen Sie nur bei einem autorisierten M.I.Hummel-Händler. Achten Sie auf die Echtheitsmerkmale. Sie sind der Beweis für exzellentes Kunsthandwerk von Goebel.

Jede echte M.I.Hummel-Figur trägt auf ihrer Unterseite das offizielle Goebel Markenzeichen.
Every authentic M.I. Hummel figurine has the official Goebel trademark on its underside.

Collectors and admirers all over the globe agree that the artistry and quality of authentic *M.I.Hummel* products are beyond compare. It is important to remember that only genuine *M.I.Hummel* figurines are created according to the strict quality control procedures established by Goebel and Sister Hummel in the 1930's.

To determine if a figurine, plate or bell is a genuine *M.I.Hummel* piece by Goebel, there are two definitive marks of identification. The first is the official Goebel trademark. Though the look of the trademarks has varied since 1935, every authentic *M.I. Hummel* figurine will have a Goebel stamp on its underside. If you don't see such a trademark, the piece is not authentic.

The other definitive identifier is that all *M.I.Hummel* items by Goebel bear the signature of Sister Maria Innocentia Hummel. When Sister Hummel made her historic contract with Franz Goebel, it was agreed that her signature – her personal stamp of approval – would appear on every piece. And so it does, to this day.

When selecting *M.I.Hummel* products, be sure to shop only at authorized *M.I.Hummel* establishments. And look carefully for these marks of authenticity. They are your assurance of the continuing excellence and artistry of Goebel.

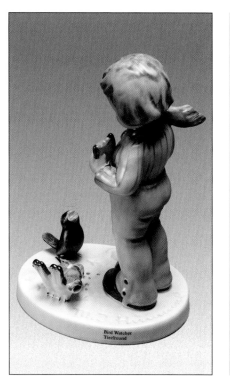

Jede echte M.I.Hummel-Figur trägt die Unterschrift von Schwester Maria Innocentia Hummel.
All M.I. Hummel items by Goebel bear the signature of Sister Maria Innocentia Hummel.

Wenn man eine Hummel-Figur umdreht, entdeckt man auf dem hellen Boden eine Reihe von Zahlen und Zeichen: Das Bodenbild.

Für gewiefte Sammler genügt oft ein Blick auf den Boden, um zu erkennen, dass sie eine besonders alte, eine seltene, eine wertvolle Figur in der Hand halten.

Vielsagend ist das Bodenbild, sozusagen der Pass einer Figur in jedem Fall. Man

muss es nur lesen können – und das ist ganz einfach. Hier ist die Bedeutung des Bodenbildes am Beispiel einer Figur Hum 530 „Land in Sicht" erklärt.

If you turn a Hummel figurine upside-down, you will discover an array of numbers and figures on the light base. A smart collector will often be able to tell, after one quick look at the base, whether he has a

particulary old, rare or valuable Hummel in his hand. You can tell a lot from the markings on the base, the so-called personal identification of each Hummel. You need to know how to read it though – and that is not difficult. Using Hum 530 "Land in Sight" as an example, we would like to explain how to interpret the markings.

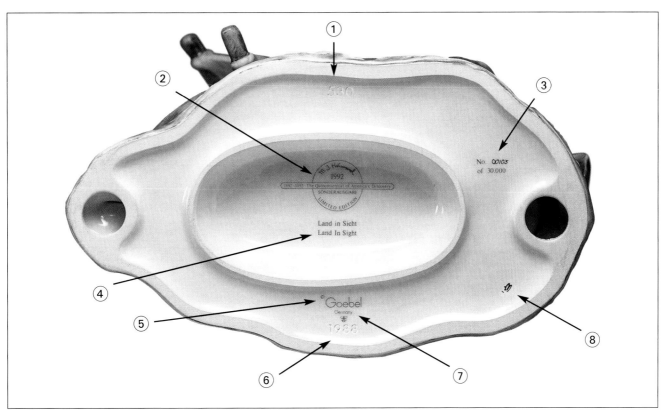

① **Modellnummer**
Jede Hummel-Figur hat eine eigene Modellnummer, die sich niemals ändert (hier Hum 530). Wird eine Figur in mehreren Größen hergestellt, hat die Modellnummer einen Schrägstrich und eine Ergänzungszahl. Bei fast allen Figuren erscheint noch eine andere Zahl, das **Garnierer-Zeichen**. Es dient der internen Qualitätskontrolle und wird im noch weichen „Scherben" angebracht.

② **Sonderbodenbild**
Man findet es bei M.I.Hummel Club-Editionen, Figuren der Century Collection, bei limitierten Sonderausgaben, auslaufenden oder neu vorgestellten Figuren und bei Jahresartikeln.

③ **Limitierte Sonderausgaben**
Diese Zahlen erscheinen nur bei limitierten Sonderausgaben. Die untere nennt die Gesamtauflage, die obere markiert das einzelne Stück innerhalb dieser Auflage.

④ **Figurenname**
Bei den Sonderausgaben ist er hier angegeben. Sonst ist er auf dem Sockel angeklebt.

⑤ **C im Kreis**
Das kleine c im Kreis bringt zum Ausdruck, dass diese Figur „urheberrechtlich" geschützt ist.

⑥ **Eingravierte Jahreszahl**
Diese Jahreszahl sagt nichts über das Herstellungsjahr aus, sondern nennt das Jahr der Entstehung von Modell und Farbmuster.

⑦ **Markenzeichen**
Das hier gezeigte Markenzeichen wurde von 1991 bis 1999 verwendet. Weil sich das Markenzeichen im Laufe der Jahre veränderte, erlaubt es den Herstellungszeitraum einer Figur zu bestimmen.

⑧ **Malerzeichen**
Die Porzellanmalerin oder der -maler, die Augen und Gesichter gestalten setzen mit der Feder ihr Zeichen auf den Boden, in der Regel mit der Jahreszahl. Sie fehlt hier, weil die Jahreszahl bereits auf dem Sonderbodenbild enthalten ist.

① **Model number**
Every Hummel has its own model number, which always stays the same. It is Hum 530 in this case. If the Hummel comes in several sizes, there is a slash after the model number, and an additional number. Most Hummels also have another number, the so called **"assembly number"**, which is used for internal quality control. It is applied when the piece is still soft.

② **Special issue marking**
This is only found on M.I.Hummel Club editions, on figurines from the Century Collection, on limited

edition issues, issues being discontinued or new edition Hummels and on annual objects.

③ **Limited edition issue**
These numbers appear only on limited edition special issues. The lower number represents the total number within the edition, and the upper number the individual figure within that collection.

④ **Name of the figurine**
The name of special issue Hummels is displayed here. Otherwise, it is attached to the side of the base.

⑤ **C in a circle**
The small c in a circle signifies that this figurine has copyright protection.

⑥ **Engraved year**
The engraved year does not refer to the year in which the Hummel was manufactured, but rather to the year when the model and colour sample came into being.

⑦ **Trademark**
This version was used from 1991 until 1999. As this marking has changed over the years, it enables you to determine the period of a figurine's production.

⑧ **Painter's symbol**
The porcelain painter who painted the face and the eyes signs the base with his nib. They usually also add the year. It was not added in this case, as it is already included in the special issue marking.

Die ersten „M.I.Hummel"-Figuren enstanden 1935. Seitdem benutzte Goebel in wechselnden Abständen immer wieder andere Bodenmarken, anhand derer das Alter einer „M.I.Hummel"-Figur in etwa bestimmt werden kann. Allerdings war der Übergang zu einer neuen Bodenmarke meist fließend. So kam es auch vor, daß für kurze Zeit noch die „alte" Bodenmarke verwendet wurde, obwohl es bereits eine „neue" gab. Manche Figuren tragen sogar doppelte Markierungen. Der genaue Zeitpunkt, ab wann die neue Marke ausschließlich verwendet wurde, läßt sich deshalb nicht genau festlegen.

The first M.I.Hummel figurines were created in 1935. The trademarks in use since then have been affixed to "M.I.Hummel" items as well as many other items produced by Goebel.

M.J.Hummel C·L·U·B®

Seit 1935 bringen die lebensfrohen, in liebevoller Handarbeit gefertigten M.I. Hummel-Figuren jeden Tag ein bisschen Sonne in die Herzen vieler Menschen, überall auf der Welt.

Menschen „erkennen" sich oder ihre Kinder und Enkelkinder in den Hummel-Figuren wieder. Vielleicht liegt hier die Erklärung, warum so gerne und immer wieder über dieses Thema gesprochen wird. Diese Faszination ist es, die zu einer Figur bald eine weitere folgen lässt. Und es ist auch die Freude, die eigene Sammlung anderen zu zeigen, um sie gemeinsam zu bewundern.

In dem Wunsch, mehr über die Welt der M.I.Hummel-Figuren zu erfahren, wenden sich die Sammler mit ihren Fragen an die W. Goebel Porzellanfabrik, suchen den Kontakt zu anderen Menschen, die sich – wie sie selbst – für diese heiteren Figuren begeisterten. Aus dieser Erfahrung entwickelte Dieter E. Schneider die Idee, einen Club für M.I.Hummel-Freunde zu gründen.

1977 wurde der „Goebel Collector's Club aus der Taufe gehoben, er bekam später den Namen M.I.Hummel Club.

Since 1935, the lively, hand-made M.I.Hummel figurines make people from all over the world feel all warm in their hart.

People "recognise" themselves, their children and grandchildren in the Hummel figurines. Maybe that is the explanation why they can't stop talking about them. This fascination makes that you will seldom see only one Hummel figurine in someone's home. It is also very nice to share your collection with other people, just admiring it together.

Always keen to know more about the world of M.I.Hummel figurines, collectors turn to the W. Goebel Porzellanfabrik with their questions, get into touch with others, who – like themselves – are enthusiastic collectors of these charming figurines. Out of this

Tarrytown, New York, USA, bis zum Sommer 1989 repräsentativer Sitz des Goebel Collectors's Club.
Tarrytown, New York, USA, head office of the Goebel Collectors's Club until summer 1989.

Dieter E. Schneider, Wilhelm Goebel und Ulrich Stocke (von links) eröffnen im Juni 1977 den Goebel Collector's Club.
Dieter E. Schneider, Wilhelm Goebel and Ulrich Stocke (from left to right) inaugurate the Goebel Collector's Club in June 1977.

experience, Dieter E. Schneider developed the idea to found a Club for the friends of M.I.Hummel.

In 1977 the "Goebel Collector's Club" is founded. Later, the name gets changed to M.I.Hummel Club.

M.I.HUMMEL CLUB

Welche Ziele hat der Club?

Der Club will informieren, den Kontakt zwischen Interessenten, Freunden und Sammlern der M.I.Hummel-Figuren pflegen und fördern. Er ist persönliche Anlaufstelle für alle Fragen, Anregungen und aktiven Gedankenaustausch. Als Sprachrohr dient die INSIGHTS, ein informatives, unterhaltsam und aufwendig gestaltetes Clubmagazin. Es erscheint vier Mal im Jahr in den Sprachversionen Deutsch, Englisch, Niederländisch und Schwedisch. Die Beiträge beschäftigen sich mit der Gestaltung und Fertigung der Figuren, mit ihrer Geschichte, mit den einzelnen Motiven oder mit den Neuerscheinungen. Mit der Firmengeschichte, den Fabrikmarken, ihrem Aussehen und ihrer Bedeutung. Und natürlich steht das Clubgeschehen im Mittelpunkt, von den regionalen Treffen der verschiedenen Lokalen Clubgruppen bis hin zu den internationalen Mitgliedertagungen, die wechselweise in Deutschland und den USA organisiert werden.

Was bietet eine Mitgliedschaft im Club?

Es steht jedem offen, Mitglied im M.I.Hummel Club zu werden. Gleich zu Beginn wird jedes neue Mitglied mit einer exklusiven Hummel-Figur begrüßt. Unter den weiteren Vorteilen einer Clubmitgliedschaft müssen an erster Stelle die exklusiven Clubeditionen erwähnt werden. Sie sind für Sammler besonders attraktiv, denn das exklusive Angebot gilt nur für ein Clubjahr.

Es liegt nahe, dass sich Clubmitglieder, die in derselben Stadt oder Region leben, kennenlernen und regelmäßig treffen. Hier hat sich eine reizvolle Form der Geselligkeit entwickelt, bei der sich die Gespräche meist auf ein Thema konzentrieren: die gemeinsame Liebe und Begeisterung für die M.I.Hummel-Figuren. Es gibt über 150 dieser Lokalen Clubgruppen in 10 Ländern.

Die exklusive Clubedition „Gesucht, gefunden" (Hum 2025/A), ist die erste Exklusivfigur einer Serie von Clubeditionen unter dem Motto „Kindheitsträume". Nur Clubmitglieder können sie erwerben.

The exclusive Club edition "Wishes Come True" (Hum 2025/A) is the first figurine in a series of exclusive Club figurines, which has "Children's dreams" as a motto. Only Club members can acquire this edition.

What are the Club's aims?

The Club wants to inform, establish and support the contact between friends and collectors of the M.I.Hummel figurines. It is the point of contact for all questions, suggestions and an active exchange of ideas. An important organ from the Club is INSIGHTS, an informative, entertaining and colourful Club magazine. There are four issues per year in German, English, Dutch and Swedish. The articles are about the production of the figurines, their history, novelties, the company's history, the trademarks, design and meaning of these marks. You can also read about the activities of the local chapters, the international member's convention, which is held alternately in Germany and the USA.

What are the benefits of a Club membership?

Everyone can join the Club. Each new member gets an exclusive Hummel figurine as a welcome gift. The exclusive Club figurines are a very important benefit. They're especially attractive to collectors, because they are only available during one Club year.

When there lives more than one member in a town, it is nearly inevitable that they get to know each other and meet regularly. When they get together, they can't stop talking about their favourite theme: the common love and enthusiasm for the M.I.Hummel figurines. There are more than 150 Local Chapters in 10 countries.

Wenn Clubmitglieder nach Rödental kommen, werden sie mit besonderer Aufmerksamkeit empfangen. Beim Rundgang durch die Ausstellung – sie zeigt zweimal jährlich wechselnde wertvolle Archivstücke – den Fertigungsvorführraum und Produktionsfilm erhalten sie genauen Einblick in die wichtigsten Produktionsschritte. Ein fränkischer Imbiss in der Goebel-Kantine gibt Gelegenheit, weitere Fragen im Gespräch mit den betreuenden Mitarbeitern zu vertiefen. Als besonderes Andenken gibt es eine „Besucherplakette" und so denkt jeder gern an dieses Erlebnis zurück.

Mittlerweile haben sich weit über 300.000 Mitglieder in über 50 Ländern dem M.I.Hummel Club angeschlossen. Am stärksten vertreten ist der Club in den USA und Kanada mit über 200.000 Mitgliedern, gefolgt von Deutschland mit 60.000 Mitgliedern. Seit seiner Gründung ist der M.I.Hummel Club noch vielseitiger und interessanter geworden. Weltweit fühlen sich die Clubmitglieder mit ihrem Hobby in der großen Familie Hummel-begeisterter Freunde gut aufgehoben. Sie verbindet ein großartiges Gemeinschaftsgefühl.

Alljährlich besucht eine Vielzahl von Clubmitgliedern die W. Goebel Porzellanfabrik in Rödental. Die Gruppen werden aufmerksam von Mitarbeitern des Clubs betreut. Das Bild entstand beim Besuch einer Gruppe aus Großbritannien.

Each year a lot of members visit the W. Goebel Porzellanfabrik in Roedental. The groups are attended by employees of the Club. This picture was taken during the visit of a British group.

When members visit us in Roedental, they get a warm welcome. A tour through the exhibition rooms – the valuable, old pieces are exchanged every half year – the demonstration room and the production film give them a good impression of the most important steps in the production of the M.I.Hummel figurines. During a Franconian lunch in the Goebel canteen, visitors have the possibility to talk with someone from the Club team about their favourite hobby. On the occasion of their visit, each member receives a "visitors-plaque" as a special keepsake to remind them of this event.

In the meantime, well over 300,000 members in more than 50 countries have joined the M.I.Hummel Club. Most members – more than 200,000 – are found in the USA and Canada, followed by Germany with 60,000 members. Since its foundation, the M.I.Hummel Club has become even more varied and interesting. All over the world, Club members are part of the big family of Hummel-enthusiastic friends. A strong sense of community connects them.

Sachkundige und freundliche Clubteams stehen den Mitgliedern in Rödental und in den USA mit Rat und Tat zur Seite.

Competent and friendly Club teams give advice and support to the members from Roedental and Pennington.

Hum 1
Geigerlein mit Hund · Puppy Love

Modell-Nr. Model No.	Größe / Size cm / inch	Modellierdatum Sculpting Date	
1	13 / 5.25	1935	CE

Anmerkung/Note:

Letzte Ausgabe 1988.

Final Issue 1988.

2/0

Hum 2
Geigerlein · Little Fiddler

Modell-Nr. Model No.	Größe / Size cm / inch	Modellierdatum Sculpting Date	
2/4/0	7,5 / 3.00	1983	CE seit / since 1998
2/0	15 / 6.00	1935	OE
2/I	19 / 7.50	1935	TWD
2/II	27 / 10.75	1935	TWD
2/III	31 / 12.25	1935	OE

Editionen mit Sonderbodenbild/ Editions with special backstamp:

Modell-Nr. Model No.	Ausgabejahr Year	Ausgabeland Country	
2/I	1996	"125 Jahre Goebel" HongKong	CE
2/I	1999	"The Guild Of Specialist" Großbritannien, United Kingdom	CE
2/I	1999	"Caribbean Collection" Karibik	CE
2/I	1999	Deutschland, Germany	CE
2/III	1998	HongKong	CE
2/III	1998	Taiwan	CE

Anmerkung/Note:

Hum 2/I Expression of Youth. CE seit 1998.

Hum 2/I Expression of Youth. CE since 1998.

Hum 2/III Offene Edition ab 2000.

Hum 2/III Open Edition 2000.

Geigerlein · Little Fiddler
Expression Of Youth

OE: Offene Edition / Open Edition
CE: Produktion beendet / Closed Edition
TWD: Vorübergehend nicht mehr in Produktion / Temporarily withdrawn from production

Modell-Nr. Model No.	Größe / Size cm / inch	Modellierdatum Sculpting Date	
3/I	12,5 / 5.00	1935	OE
3/II	20 / 8.00	1935	TWD
3/III	23 / 9.00	1935	TWD

Editionen mit Sonderbodenbild/ Editions with special backstamp:

Modell-Nr. Model No.	Ausgabejahr Year	Ausgabeort Country	
3/III	1997	"5th Club Anniversary" HongKong	CE
3/III	1997	"Special Edition" Taiwan	CE

Hum 3
Der Bücherwurm · Book Worm

Modell-Nr. Model No.	Größe / Size cm / inch	Modellierdatum Sculpting Date	
4	12,5 / 5.00	1935	OE

Hum 4
Geigerlein · Little Fiddler

Modell-Nr. Model No.	Größe / Size cm / inch	Modellierdatum Sculpting Date	
5	12 / 4.75	1935	CE

Anmerkung/Note:

Letzte Ausgabe 1989.

Final Issue 1989.

Hum 5
Wanderbub · Strolling Along

OE: Offene Edition / Open Edition
CE: Produktion beendet / Closed Edition
TWD: Vorübergehend nicht mehr in Produktion / Temporarily withdrawn from production

Modell-Nr. Model No.	Größe / Size cm / inch	Modellierdatum Sculpting Date	
6/2/0	10 / 4.00	1983	OE
6/0	12 / 4.75	1935	OE
6/I	14 / 5.50	1935	TWD seit / since 1998
6/II	18,5 / 7.25	1935	CE

6/0

Hum 6
Jägerlein · Sensitive Hunter

Modell-Nr. Model No.	Größe / Size cm / inch	Modellierdatum Sculpting Date	
7/0	15 / 6.00	1935	OE
7/I	18 / 7.00	1935	TWD
7/II	24 / 9.50	1935	TWD
7/III	28,5 / 11.25	1935	OE
7/X	84 / 33.00	1969	OE

7/0

Hum 7
Wanderbub · Merry Wanderer

Editionen mit Sonderbodenbild/ Editions with special backstamp:

Modell-Nr. Model No.	Ausgabejahr Year	Ausgabeland Country	
7/0	1996	St. Thomas, Karibik, Caribbean	CE
7/0	1996	QVC USA, Expression Of Youth	CE
7/I	1996	QVC USA, Expression Of Youth	CE
7/I	1996	"125 Jahre Goebel" HongKong	CE
7/I	1998	Großbritannien, United Kingdom	CE
7/I	1999	"Caribbean Collection" Karibik	CE
7/III	1997	"Mery Wanderer Going Home" HongKong	CE
7/III	1997	"Limited Edition" Taiwan	CE

Wanderbub · Merry Wanderer
Expression Of Youth

Anmerkung/Note:

Hum 7/I Expression of Youth. CE seit 1998.

Expression of Youth. CE since 1998.

OE: Offene Edition / Open Edition
CE: Produktion beendet / Closed Edition
TWD: Vorübergehend nicht mehr in Produktion / Temporarily withdrawn from production

Modell-Nr. Model No.	Größe / Size cm / inch	Modellierdatum Sculpting Date	
8/I	10 / 4.00	1935	OE

Hum 8
Der Bücherwurm · Book Worm

Editionen mit Sonderbodenbild/ Editions with special backstamp:

Modell-Nr. Model No.	Ausgabejahr Year	Ausgabeort Country	
8	1999	"Caribbean Collection" Karibik	CE

Modell-Nr. Model No.	Größe / Size cm / inch	Modellierdatum Sculpting Date	
9	14 / 5.50	1935	TWD seit / since 1999

Hum 9
Gratulant · Begging His Share

Modell-Nr. Model No.	Größe / Size cm / inch	Modellierdatum Sculpting Date	
10/I	21 / 8.25	1935	TWD seit / since 1999
10/III	32,5 / 12.75	1935	CE

Editionen mit Sonderbodenbild/ Editions with special backstamp:

Modell-Nr. Model No.	Ausgabejahr Year	Ausgabeort Country	
10/I	1996	"A Memorial Tribute" USA	CE

Hum 10
Blumenmadonna · Flower Madonna

Anmerkung/Note:

Ohne Dekoration oder mit Umhang in den Farben blau, braun, pastellgelb oder

elfenbeinfarben.

Without decoration or with blue, brown, pastel yellow or ivory coat.

Modell-Nr. Model No.	Größe / Size cm / inch	Modellierdatum Sculpting Date	
11/2/0	10,5 / 4.00	1935	OE
11/0	12 / 4.75	1935	OE

Editionen mit Sonderbodenbild/ Editions with special backstamp:

Modell-Nr. Model No.	Ausgabejahr Year	Ausgabeort Country	
11/2/0	1995	QVC, Großbritannien, United Kingdom USA	CE
11/2/0	2000	USA, 130 Jahre Goebel	OE

Hum 11
Wanderbub · Merry Wanderer

11/0

Modell-Nr. Model No.	Größe / Size cm / inch	Modellierdatum Sculpting Date	
12/2/0	10 / 4.00	1935	OE
12/I	14 / 5.50	1935	OE

Editionen mit Sonderbodenbild/ Editions with special backstamp:

Modell-Nr. Model No.	Ausgabejahr Year	Ausgabeland Country	
12/2/0	1992/93	USA	CE
12/2/0	1999	Deutschland, Germany	CE
12/2/0	2000	USA	CE

Hum 12
Ich bringe Glück, Kaminfeger
Chimney Sweep

12/0

Modell-Nr. Model No.	Größe / Size cm / inch	Modellierdatum Sculpting Date	
13/2/0	11 / 4.25	1962	OE
13/0	13,5 / 5.25	1935	OE
13/II	17,5 / 6.75	1935	TWD
13/V	35 / 13.75	1955	OE

Hum 13
Die Gratulantin · Meditation

13/0

OE: Offene Edition / Open Edition
CE: Produktion beendet / Closed Edition
TWD: Vorübergehend nicht mehr in Produktion / Temporarily withdrawn from production

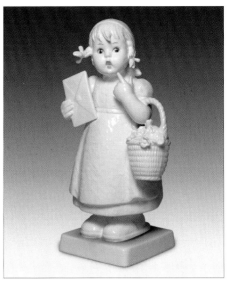

Die Gratulantin · Meditation
Expression Of Youth

Editionen mit Sonderbodenbild/ Editions with special backstamp:

Modell-Nr. Model No.	Ausgabejahr Year	Ausgabeland Country	
13/2/0	1999	Deutschland, Germany	CE
13/0	1999	Deutschland, Germany	CE
13/II	2000	"Millennium Revival Collection"	OE
13/V	2000	"125 Jahre Goebel" HongKong	CE
13/V	1999	"Caribbean Collection" Karibik	CE

Anmerkung/Note:

Hum 13/V Expression of Youth. CE seit 1998.

Expression of Youth. CE since 1998.

Hum 14/ B, A
Der Bücherwurm · Bookworm
Buchstützen · Book Ends

Modell-Nr. Model No.	Größe / Size cm / inch	Modellierdatum Sculpting Date		
14/A	14 / 5.50	1935	TWD	Junge, Boy
14/B	14 / 5.50	1935	TWD	Mädchen, Girl

15/0

Hum 15
Hört Ihr Leute, Nachtwächter
Hear Ye, Hear Ye

Modell-Nr. Model No.	Größe / Size cm / inch	Modellierdatum Sculpting Date	
15/2/0	10,5 / 4.00	1983	OE
15/0	13 / 5.25	1935	OE
15/I	15.5 / 6.00	1935	TWD seit 1998 / since 1998
15/II	19 / 7.50	1935	TWD

OE: Offene Edition / Open Edition
CE: Produktion beendet / Closed Edition
TWD: Vorübergehend nicht mehr in Produktion / Temporarily withdrawn from production

Hört Ihr Leute, Nachtwächter
Hear Ye, Hear Ye
Expression Of Youth

Editionen mit Sonderbodenbild/ Editions with special backstamp:

Modell-Nr. Model No.	Ausgabejahr Year	Ausgabeland Country	
15/0	1999	Deutschland, Germany	CE
15/2/0	1999	"Rodach", Deutschland, Germany	CE
15/I	1996	QVC, USA	CE
15/I	1999	"Rodach", Deutschland, Germany	CE
15/II	1996	"125 Jahre Goebel" HongKong	CE
15/II	1999	Großbritannien, United Kingdom	CE

Anmerkung/Note:

Hum 15/II Auch als Expression of Youth. CE seit 1998.

Also available as Expression of Youth. CE since 1998.

Hum 16
Hans im Glück · Little Hiker

Modell-Nr. Model No.	Größe / Size cm / inch	Modellierdatum Sculpting Date	
16/2/0	10 / 4.00	1935	OE
16/I	14 / 5.50	1935	TWD seit 1998 / since 1998

Hum 17
Ich gratuliere · Congratulations

Modell-Nr. Model No.	Größe / Size cm / inch	Modellierdatum Sculpting Date	
17/0	14 / 5.50	1935	CE
17/II		1935	CE

Anmerkung/Note:

Hum 17/0 Letzte Ausgabe 1999, Sonderbodenbild und Plombe im letzten Produktionsjahr.

Final Issue 1999, special backstamp and medallion in the last year of production.

OE: Offene Edition / Open Edition
CE: Produktion beendet / Closed Edition
TWD: Vorübergehend nicht mehr in Produktion / Temporarily withdrawn from production

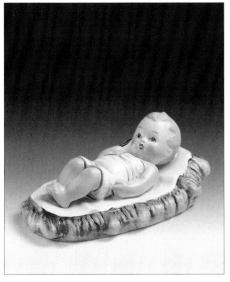

Modell-Nr. Model No.	Größe / Size cm / inch	Modellierdatum Sculpting Date	
18	5 x 15 / 2.00 x 6.00	1985	TWD seit 1998 / since 1998

Hum 18
Stille Nacht, Christkind · Christ Child

Modell-Nr. Model No.	Größe / Size cm / inch	Modellierdatum Sculpting Date	
20	11 / 4.25	1935	OE

Editionen mit Sonderbodenbild/ Editions with special backstamp:

Modell-Nr. Model No.	Ausgabejahr Year	Ausgabeland Country	
20	1998	"Wiesbaden" US Militär, US Military	CE

Hum 20
Der fromme Reitersmann
Prayer Before Battle

21/II

Modell-Nr. Model No.	Größe / Size cm / inch	Modellierdatum Sculpting Date	
21/0	10 / 4.00	1935	OE
21/0/1/2	15 / 6.00	1935	OE
21/I	18 / 7.00	1935	TWD seit 1999 / since 1999
21/II	22 / 8.75	1935	TWD

Hum 21
Christkindlein kommt · Heavenly Angel

OE: Offene Edition / Open Edition
CE: Produktion beendet / Closed Edition
TWD: Vorübergehend nicht mehr in Produktion / Temporarily withdrawn from production

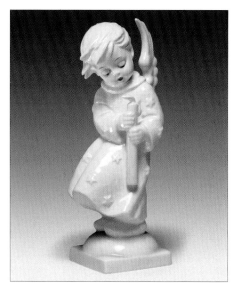

Christkindlein kommt · Heavenly Angel
Expression Of Youth

Editionen mit Sonderbodenbild/ Editions with special backstamp:

Modell-Nr. Model No.	Ausgabejahr Year	Ausgabeland Country	
21/II	1935	"Caribbean Collection" Karibik	CE

Anmerkung/Note:

Hum 21/II Expression of Youth. CE seit 1998.

Expression of Youth. CE since 1998.

Hum 22
Sitzender Engel · Sitting Angel
Weihkessel · Holy Water Font

Modell-Nr. Model No.	Größe / Size cm / inch	Modellierdatum Sculpting Date	
22/0	9 / 3.50	1935	OE
22/I	12 / 4.75	1935	CE seit 1998 / since 1998

23/I

Hum 23
Bei Mutter Maria, Marterl · Adoration

Modell-Nr. Model No.	Größe / Size cm / inch	Modellierdatum Sculpting Date	
23/I	16 / 6.25	1935	OE
23/III	23 / 9.00	1935	TWD seit 1998 / since 1998

OE: Offene Edition / Open Edition
CE: Produktion beendet / Closed Edition
TWD: Vorübergehend nicht mehr in Produktion / Temporarily withdrawn from production

Modell-Nr. Model No.	Größe / Size cm / inch	Modellierdatum Sculpting Date	
24/I	9 x 13	1935	TWD seit 1998 / since 1998
	3.50 x 5.25		
24/III	16 / 6.25	1935	TWD

Hum 24
Wiegenlied · Lullaby
Kerzenhalter · Candle Holder

Modell-Nr. Model No.	Größe / Size cm / inch	Modellierdatum Sculpting Date	
25	9 x 13	1935	TWD
	3.50 x 5.25		

Hum 25
Stille Nacht · Angelic Sleep
Kerzenhalter · Candle Holder

Modell-Nr. Model No.	Größe / Size cm / inch	Modellierdatum Sculpting Date	
26/0	13 / 5.25	1935	TWD seit 1998 / since 1998
26/I	15 / 6.00	1935	CE seit 1998 / since 1998

Hum 26
Jesuskind · Child Jesus
Weihkessel · Holy Water Font

OE: Offene Edition / Open Edition
CE: Produktion beendet / Closed Edition
TWD: Vorübergehend nicht mehr in Produktion / Temporarily withdrawn from production

Hum 27
O, du fröhliche... · Joyous News

Modell-Nr. Model No.	Größe / Size cm / inch	Modellierdatum Sculpting Date	
27/I	6,5 / 2.50	1935	CE
27/III	12 / 4.75	1935	TWD seit 1999 / since 1999

Anmerkung/Note:

27/I Kerzenhalter.

    Candle Holder.

Hum 28
Abendlied, Marterl · Wayside Devotion

Modell-Nr. Model No.	Größe / Size cm / inch	Modellierdatum Sculpting Date	
28/II	19 / 7.50	1935	OE
28/III	21 / 8.25	1935	TWD seit 1998 / since 1998

Hum 29
Schutzengel · Guardian Angel
Weihkessel · Holy Water Font

Modell-Nr. Model No.	Größe / Size cm / inch	Modellierdatum Sculpting Date	
29/0	15 / 6.00	1935	CE
29/I	16,5 / 6.50	1935	CE

OE: Offene Edition / Open Edition
CE: Produktion beendet / Closed Edition
TWD: Vorübergehend nicht mehr in Produktion / Temporarily withdrawn from production

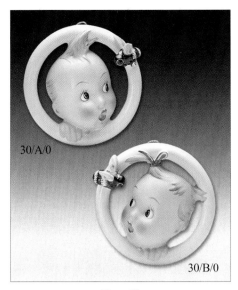

30/A/0

30/B/0

Modell-Nr. Model No.	Größe / Size cm / inch	Modellierdatum Sculpting Date		
30/A/0	13 / 5.25	1935	OE	Junge, Boy
30/B/0	13 / 5.25	1935	OE	Mädchen, Girl
30/A/I	14 / 5.50	1935	CE	Junge, Boy
30/B/I	14 / 5.50	1935	CE	Mädchen, Girl

Hum 30
Hui, die Hummel · Ba-Bee Ring
Wandring · Wall Plaque

Modell-Nr. Model No.	Größe / Size cm / inch	Modellierdatum Sculpting Date	
31	9 / 3.50	1935	CE

Hum 31
Stille Nacht · Silent Night
Kerzenhalter · Candle Holder

Modell-Nr. Model No.	Größe / Size cm / inch	Modellierdatum Sculpting Date	
32/0	13 / 5.25	1935	TWD seit 1998 / since 1998
32/I	15 / 6.00	1935	CE

Hum 32
O, du fröhliche...Engel · Little Gabriel

OE: Offene Edition / Open Edition
CE: Produktion beendet / Closed Edition
TWD: Vorübergehend nicht mehr in Produktion / Temporarily withdrawn from production

Modell-Nr. Model No.	Größe / Size cm / inch	Modellierdatum Sculpting Date	
I/39/0	5 / 2.00	1935	OE
III/39/0	5 / 2.00	1935	CE
III/39/I	7 / 2.75	1951	CE seit 1998 / since 1998

Sonderversion / Special Edition

Modell-Nr. Model No.	Ausgabejahr Year	Ausgabeland Country	
II/39/0	1992	USA	CE

Anmerkung/Note:

Kerzenhalter.

Candle Holder.

Hum 39
Adventsengelchen mit Bandoneon
Angel With Bandoneon

Modell-Nr. Model No.	Größe / Size cm / inch	Modellierdatum Sculpting Date	
I/40/0	5 / 2.00	1935	OE
III/40/0	5 / 2.00	1935	CE
III/40/I	6,5 / 2.75	1951	CE seit 1998 / since 1998

Sonderversion / Special Edition

Modell-Nr. Model No.	Ausgabejahr Year	Ausgabeland Country	
II/40/0	1992	USA	CE

Anmerkung/Note:

Kerzenhalter.
Candle Holder.

Hum 40
Adventsengelchen mit Trompete
Angel With Trumpet

Modell-Nr. Model No.	Größe / Size cm / inch	Modellierdatum Sculpting Date	
42/0	16 / 6.25	1935	TWD seit 1998 / since 1998
42/I	19,5 / 7.75	1935	CE

OE: Offene Edition / Open Edition
CE: Produktion beendet / Closed Edition
TWD: Vorübergehend nicht mehr in Produktion / Temporarily withdrawn from production

Hum 42
Der gute Hirte · Good Shepherd

Modell-Nr. Model No.	Größe / Size cm / inch	Modellierdatum Sculpting Date	
43/5/0	7 / 2.75	1991	CE
43/0	13 / 5.25	1935	OE

Hum 43
Lausbub · March Winds

Modell-Nr. Model No.	Größe / Size cm / inch	Modellierdatum Sculpting Date	
44/A	24 / 9.50	1935	TWD

Hum 44 A
Apfeldieb · Culprits
Tischlampe · Table Lamp

Modell-Nr. Model No.	Größe / Size cm / inch	Modellierdatum Sculpting Date	
44/B	24 / 9.50	1950	TWD

Hum 44 B
In Sicherheit · Out Of Danger
Tischlampe · Table Lamp

OE: Offene Edition / Open Edition
CE: Produktion beendet / Closed Edition
TWD: Vorübergehend nicht mehr in Produktion / Temporarily withdrawn from production

Modell-Nr. Model No.	Größe / Size cm / inch	Modellierdatum Sculpting Date	
45/0	30 / 11.75	1952	TWD
45/I/W	30,5 / 12.00	1935	TWD
45/I/6	30,5 / 12.00	1952	OE
45/III/6	42 / 16.50	1935	CE seit 1998 / since 1998
45/III/W	42 / 16.50	1935	CE seit 1998 / since 1998

Anmerkung/Note:

45/0	weiß, blau, rot, gelb • white, blue, red, yellow.
45/I/6 45/III/6	blaue Dekoration • blue decoration
45/I/W 45/III/W	weiße Dekoration • white decoration

Hum 45
Madonna mit Heiligenschein
Madonna With Halo

Modell-Nr. Model No.	Größe / Size cm / inch	Modellierdatum Sculpting Date	
46/0	27 / 10.75	1952	TWD
46/I/6	29,5 / 11.50	1935	TWD
46/I/W	29,5 / 11.50	1935	TWD
46/III/6	37,5 / 14.75	1935	CE
46/III/W	37,5 / 14.75	1935	CE

Anmerkung/Note:

46/0	weiß, blau, rot, gelb • white, blue, red, yellow.
46/I/6 46/III/6	blaue Dekoration • blue decoration
46/I/W 46/III/W	weiße Dekoration • white decoration

Hum 46
Madonna ohne Heiligenschein
Madonna Without Halo

47/0

Modell-Nr. Model No.	Größe / Size cm / inch	Modellierdatum Sculpting Date	
47/3/0	10 / 4.00	1936	OE
47/0	12 / 4.75	1936	OE
47/II	19 / 7.50	1936	TWD

Hum 47
Gänseliesl · Goose Girl

OE: Offene Edition / Open Edition
CE: Produktion beendet / Closed Edition
TWD: Vorübergehend nicht mehr in Produktion / Temporarily withdrawn from production

Gänseliesl · Goose Girl
Expression Of Youth

Modell-Nr. Model No.	Ausgabejahr Year	Ausgabeort Country	
47/II	1996	"125 Jahre Goebel" HongKong	CE
47/II	1999	Großbritannien, United Kingdom	CE
47/II		Deutschland, Germany	CE

Anmerkung/Note:

Hum 47/II Expression of Youth. CE seit 1998.

Expression of Youth. CE since 1998.

Hum 48
Madonnenbild · Madonna
Wandbild · Wall Plaque

Modell-Nr. Model No.	Größe / Size cm / inch	Modellierdatum Sculpting Date	
48/0	10 / 4.00	1936	TWD
48/II	15 / 6.00	1936	CE seit 1998 / since 1998
48/V	28,5 / 11.25	1936	CE seit 1998 / since 1998

49/0

Hum 49
Brüderlein und Schwesterlein · To Market

Modell-Nr. Model No.	Größe / Size cm / inch	Modellierdatum Sculpting Date	
49/3/0	11 / 4.25	1936	
49/0	14 / 5.50	1936	TWD seit 1998 / since 1998
49/I	16,5 / 6.50	1936	TWD

Editionen mit Sonderbodenbild/ Editions with special backstamp:

Modell-Nr. Model No.	Ausgabejahr Year	Ausgabeort Country	
49/3/0	1997	"Hertogenbosch" Niederlande, Netherlands	CE
49/I	2000	"Millennium Revival Collection"	OE

OE: Offene Edition / Open Edition
CE: Produktion beendet / Closed Edition
TWD: Vorübergehend nicht mehr in Produktion / Temporarily withdrawn from production

Hum 50
Soldatenspiel · Volunteers

Modell-Nr. Model No.	Größe / Size cm / inch	Modellierdatum Sculpting Date	
50/2/0	12,5 / 5.00	1936	OE
50/0	14 / 5.50	1936	OE
50/I	16,5 / 6.50	1936	TWD

Editionen mit Sonderbodenbild/ Editions with special backstamp:

Modell-Nr. Model No.	Ausgabejahr Year	Ausgabeland Country	
50/2/0	1992	"Desert Shield - Desert Storm" US Militär, US Military	CE
50/2/0	1991	Militär, Military	CE

Hum 51
Dorfbub · Village Boy

Modell-Nr. Model No.	Größe / Size cm / inch	Modellierdatum Sculpting Date	
51/5/0	7,5 / 3.00	1991	CE
51/3/0	10 / 4.00	1936	OE
51/2/0	13 /5.25	1961	OE
51/0	16 / 6.25	1936	TWD seit 1998 / since 1998
51/I	19 / 7.50	1936	TWD

Editionen mit Sonderbodenbild/ Editions with special backstamp:

Modell-Nr. Model No.	Ausgabejahr Year	Ausgabeland Country	
51/I	2000	"Millennium Revival Collection"	OE

Hum 52
Hausmütterchen · Going To Grandma's

Modell-Nr. Model No.	Größe / Size cm / inch	Modellierdatum Sculpting Date	
52/0	12 / 4.75	1936	OE
52/I	16,5 / 6.50	1936	TWD

Editionen mit Sonderbodenbild/ Editions with special backstamp:

Modell-Nr. Model No.	Ausgabejahr Year	Ausgabeland Country	
51/I	2000	"Millennium Revival Collection"	OE

OE: Offene Edition / Open Edition
CE: Produktion beendet / Closed Edition
TWD: Vorübergehend nicht mehr in Produktion / Temporarily withdrawn from production

Hum 53
Gesangsprobe · Joyful

Modell-Nr. Model No.	Größe / Size cm / inch	Modellierdatum Sculpting Date	
53	10 / 4.00	1936	OE
III/53	16 / 6.25	1936	TWD
IV/53	14 / 5.50	1995	CE

Editionen mit Sonderbodenbild/ Editions with special backstamp:

Modell-Nr. Model No.	Ausgabejahr Year	Ausgabeort Country	
IV/53	1998	"M.I.Hummel Club Tagung 1998" Deutschland, Germany	CE

Hum III/53
Gesangsprobe · Joyful
Dose · Box

Anmerkung/Note:

III/53 Dose, Box.

IV/53 Musikdose, auf 29.900 Stück weltweit limitiert und einzeln nummeriert.

Music Box, worldwide limited and numbered edition of 29,900 pcs.

Hum IV/53
Gesangsprobe · Joyful
Musikdose · Music Box

Hum 54
Stille Nacht, Krippe · Silent Night
Kerzenhalter · Candle Holder

Modell-Nr. Model No.	Größe / Size cm / inch	Modellierdatum Sculpting Date	
54	9 x 12 3.50 x 4.75	1936	TWD seit 1998 / since 1998

OE: Offene Edition / Open Edition
CE: Produktion beendet / Closed Edition
TWD: Vorübergehend nicht mehr in Produktion / Temporarily withdrawn from production

Hum 58
Hasenvater · Playmates

Modell-Nr. Model No.	Größe / Size cm / inch	Modellierdatum Sculpting Date	
58/2/0	9 / 3.50	1983	OE
58/0	10 / 4.00	1936	OE
58/I	11 / 4.25	1936	TWD seit / since 1998
III/58	16 / 6.25	1936	CE
IV/58	15.5 / 6.25	1995	CE

Editionen mit Sonderbodenbild/ Editions with special backstamp:

Modell-Nr. Model No.	Ausgabejahr Year	Ausgabeort Country	
58/0	1994	"M.I.Hummel Club Tagung 1994" Deutschland, Germany	CE
III/58	1996	Danbury, USA	CE

Hum III/58
Hasenvater · Playmates
Dose · Box

Anmerkung/Note:

III/58 Dose, Box.

IV/58 Musikdose, auf 29.900 Stück weltweit limitiert und einzeln nummeriert.

Music Box, worldwide limited and numbered edition of 29,900 pcs.

Hum IV/58
Hasenvater · Playmates
Musikdose · Music Box

Hum 59
Ski-Heil · Skier

Modell-Nr. Model No.	Größe / Size cm / inch	Modellierdatum Sculpting Date	
59	14 / 5.50	1936	OE

OE: Offene Edition / Open Edition
CE: Produktion beendet / Closed Edition
TWD: Vorübergehend nicht mehr in Produktion / Temporarily withdrawn from production

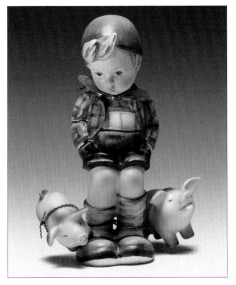

Modell-Nr. Model No.	Größe / Size cm / inch	Modellierdatum Sculpting Date	
60/A	12,5 / 5.00	1936	CE

Hum 60/A
Schweinehirt · Farm Boy
Buchstützen · Book Ends

Modell-Nr. Model No.	Größe / Size cm / inch	Modellierdatum Sculpting Date	
60/B	12,5 / 5.00	1936	CE

Hum 60/B
Gänseliesl · Goose Girl
Buchstützen · Book Ends

Modell-Nr. Model No.	Größe / Size cm / inch	Modellierdatum Sculpting Date	
61/A		1936	CE

Hum 61/A
Hasenvater · Playmates
Buchstützen · Book Ends

OE: Offene Edition / Open Edition
CE: Produktion beendet / Closed Edition
TWD: Vorübergehend nicht mehr in Produktion / Temporarily withdrawn from production

Modell-Nr. Model No.	Größe / Size cm / inch	Modellierdatum Sculpting Date	
61/B		1936	CE

Hum 61/B
Kükenmütterchen · Chick Girl
Buchstützen · Book Ends

Modell-Nr. Model No.	Größe / Size cm / inch	Modellierdatum Sculpting Date	
62	9 / 3.50	1936	TWD

Hum 62
Strickliesl · Happy Pastime
Aschenbecher · Ashtray

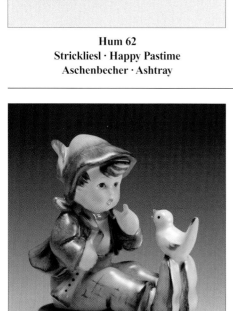

Modell-Nr. Model No.	Größe / Size cm / inch	Modellierdatum Sculpting Date	
63	7.5 / 3.00	1937	OE
III/63	15 / 6.00	1937	TWD
IV/63	13.5 / 5.25	1994	CE

Editionen mit Sonderbodenbild/ Editions with special backstamp:

Modell-Nr. Model No.	Ausgabejahr Year	Ausgabeort Country	
IV/63	1998	"M.I.Hummel Club Tagung 1998" Deutschland, Germany	CE

Hum 63
's stimmt net · Singing Lesson

OE: Offene Edition / Open Edition
CE: Produktion beendet / Closed Edition
TWD: Vorübergehend nicht mehr in Produktion / Temporarily withdrawn from production

III/63

Anmerkung/Note:

III/63 Dose, Box.

IV/63 Musikdose, auf 29.900 Stück weltweit limitiert und einzeln nummeriert.

Music Box, worldwide limited and numbered edition of 29,900 pcs.

IV/63

Hum III/63
's stimmt net · Singing Lesson
Dose · Box

Hum IV/63
's stimmt net · Singing Lesson
Musikdose · Music Box

Modell-Nr. Model No.	Größe / Size cm / inch	Modellierdatum Sculpting Date	
64	14 / 5.50	1937	OE

Hum 64
Schäferbub · Shepherd's Boy

Modell-Nr. Model No.	Größe / Size cm / inch	Modellierdatum Sculpting Date	
65/0	10,5 / 4.25	1956	CE
65/I	12 / 4.75	1937	CE

Anmerkung/Note:

Letzte Ausgabe 1993, Sonderbodenbild und Plombe im letzten Produktionsjahr.

Final Issue 1993, special backstamp and medallion in the last year of production.

Hum 65
Auf Wiedersehen · Farewell

OE: Offene Edition / Open Edition
CE: Produktion beendet / Closed Edition
TWD: Vorübergehend nicht mehr in Produktion / Temporarily withdrawn from production

Modell-Nr. Model No.	Größe / Size cm / inch	Modellierdatum Sculpting Date	
66	13 / 5.25	1937	OE

Editionen mit Sonderbodenbild/ Editions with special backstamp:

Modell-Nr. Model No.	Ausgabejahr Year	Ausgabeort Country	
66	1999	"Schweinfurt"	CE
		US Militär, US Military	

Hum 66
Schweinehirt · Farm Boy

Modell-Nr. Model No.	Größe / Size cm / inch	Modellierdatum Sculpting Date	
67	11,5 / 4.50	1937	OE

Editionen mit Sonderbodenbild/ Editions with special backstamp:

Modell-Nr. Model No.	Ausgabejahr Year	Ausgabeort Country	
67	1997	"60th Anniversary"	CE
		Weltweit, Worldwide	

Hum 67
Puppenmütterchen · Doll Mother

Modell-Nr. Model No.	Größe / Size cm / inch	Modellierdatum Sculpting Date	
68/2/0	11 / 4.25	1962	CE
68/0	14 / 5.50	1937	CE

Anmerkung/Note:

Letzte Ausgabe 1992, Sonderbodenbild und Plombe im letzten Produktionsjahr.

Final Issue 1992, special backstamp and medallion in the last year of production.

Hum 68
Schäferbub · Lost Sheep

OE: Offene Edition / Open Edition
CE: Produktion beendet / Closed Edition
TWD: Vorübergehend nicht mehr in Produktion / Temporarily withdrawn from production

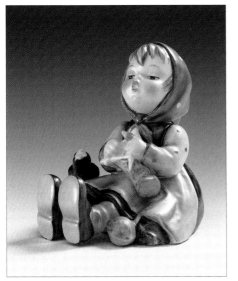

Modell-Nr. Model No.	Größe / Size cm / inch	Modellierdatum Sculpting Date	
69	9 / 3.50	1937	CE
III/69	15 / 6.00	1937	TWD

Anmerkung/Note:

Hum 69 Letzte Ausgabe 1996,
Sonderbodenbild und Plombe im letzten
Produktionsjahr.

Hum 69 Final Issue 1996,
special backstamp and medaillon in the
last year of production.

III/69 Dose, Box

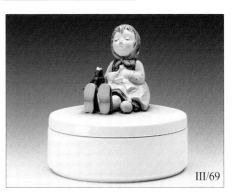

Hum III/69

Hum 69
Strickliesl · Happy Pastime

Hum III/69
Strickliesl · Happy Pastime
Dose · Box

Modell-Nr. Model No.	Größe / Size cm / inch	Modellierdatum Sculpting Date	
70	18 / 7.00	1937	TWD seit / since 1998

Hum 70
Jesulein · The Holy Child

71/I

Modell-Nr. Model No.	Größe / Size cm / inch	Modellierdatum Sculpting Date	
71/2/0	12 / 4.75	1983	OE
71/I	15 / 6.00	1937	OE

Editionen mit Sonderbodenbild/ Editions with special backstamp:

Modell-Nr. Model No.	Ausgabejahr Year	Ausgabeort Country	
71/2/0	1997	QVC, USA	CE

Hum 71
Unter einem Dach · Stormy Weather

OE: Offene Edition / Open Edition
CE: Produktion beendet / Closed Edition
TWD: Vorübergehend nicht mehr in Produktion / Temporarily withdrawn from production

Modell-Nr. Model No.	Größe / Size cm / inch	Modellierdatum Sculpting Date	
72	13 / 5.25	1937	TWD

Hum 72
Frühling ist's · Spring Cheer

Modell-Nr. Model No.	Größe / Size cm / inch	Modellierdatum Sculpting Date	
73	11 / 4.25	1937	OE

Hum 73
Fleißiges Lieschen · Little Helper

Modell-Nr. Model No.	Größe / Size cm / inch	Modellierdatum Sculpting Date	
74	11 / 4.25	1937	OE

Editionen mit Sonderbodenbild/ Editions with special backstamp:

Modell-Nr. Model No.	Ausgabejahr Year	Ausgabeort Country	
74	1992	"Special Event" USA	CE
74	1992	"Malvorführung, Artist Promotion" Deutschland, Germany	CE
74	1998	Irland, Ireland	CE

Hum 74
Die kleine Gärtnerin · Little Gardener

OE: Offene Edition / Open Edition
CE: Produktion beendet / Closed Edition
TWD: Vorübergehend nicht mehr in Produktion / Temporarily withdrawn from production

Modell-Nr. Model No.	Größe / Size cm / inch	Modellierdatum Sculpting Date		
75	9 / 3.50	1937		TWD seit / since 1998

Hum 75
Weißer Engel · White Angel
Weihkessel · Holy Water Font

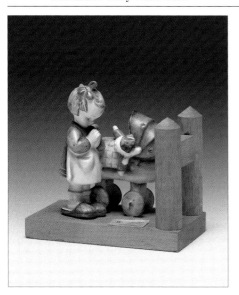

Modell-Nr. Model No.	Größe / Size cm / inch	Modellierdatum Sculpting Date	
76/A	12 / 4.75	1938	CE

Anmerkung/Note:

Kein Verkauf, nur Musterfertigung.

Never distributed, archives samples only.

Hum 76/A
Puppenmütterchen · Doll Mother
Buchstützen · Book Ends

Keine Archivmuster vorhanden.

No Samples available in our Archives.

Modell-Nr. Model No.	Größe / Size cm / inch	Modellierdatum Sculpting Date	
76/B	12 / 4.75	1938	CE

Anmerkung/Note:

Kein Verkauf, nur Musterfertigung.

Never distributed, archives samples only.

Hum 76/B
Der fromme Reitersmann · Buchstützen
Prayer Before Battle · Book Ends

OE: Offene Edition / Open Edition
CE: Produktion beendet / Closed Edition
TWD: Vorübergehend nicht mehr in Produktion / Temporarily withdrawn from production

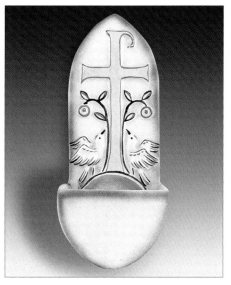

Modell-Nr. Model No.	Größe / Size cm / inch	Modellierdatum Sculpting Date	
77		1937	CE

Hum 77
Kreuz mit Tauben · Cross With Doves
Weihkessel · Holy Water Font

Anmerkung/Note:

Kein Verkauf, nur Musterfertigung.

Never distributed, archives samples only.

Modell-Nr. Model No.	Größe / Size cm / inch	Modellierdatum Sculpting Date	
78/0	6 / 2.25	1988	TWD
78/I	6,5 / 2.50	1937	TWD
78/II/¹/₂	11 / 4.25	1964	TWD
78/II	8,5 / 3.25	1987	TWD
78/III	13 / 5.25	1937	TWD
78/V	19,5 / 7.75	1937	TWD
78/VI	28,5 / 11.25	1964	TWD
78/VIII	33,5 / 13.25	1937	TWD

Hum 78
Christkind · Blessed Child

Modell-Nr. Model No.	Größe / Size cm / inch	Modellierdatum Sculpting Date	
79	13 / 5.25	1937	CE

Anmerkung/Note:

Letzte Ausgabe 1991, Sonderbodenbild und Plombe im letzten Produktionsjahr.

Final Issue 1991, special backstamp and medallion in the last year of production.

Hum 79
Hinaus in die Ferne · Globe Trotter

OE: Offene Edition / Open Edition
CE: Produktion beendet / Closed Edition
TWD: Vorübergehend nicht mehr in Produktion / Temporarily withdrawn from production

Modell-Nr. Model No.	Größe / Size cm / inch	Modellierdatum Sculpting Date	
80	14 / 5.50	1937	OE

Hum 80
Erster Schulgang (Junge) · Little Scholar

81/0

Hum 81
Erster Schulgang (Mädchen) · School Girl

Modell-Nr. Model No.	Größe / Size cm / inch	Modellierdatum Sculpting Date	
81/2/0	11 / 4.25	1937	OE
81/0	13 / 5.25	1937	OE

Editionen mit Sonderbodenbild/ Editions with special backstamp:

Modell-Nr. Model No.	Ausgabejahr Year	Ausgabeland Country	
81/2/0	1996	"125" USA	CE
81/2/0	1996	" International Collectible Exposition" USA	CE
81/2/0	1998	QVC, USA	CE
81/0	1998	QVC, USA	CE

82/0

Hum 82
Schulschwänzer · School Boy

Modell-Nr. Model No.	Größe / Size cm / inch	Modellierdatum Sculpting Date	
82/2/0	11 / 4.25	1938	OE
82/0	13 / 5.25	1938	OE
82/II	20 / 8.00	1938	TWD seit / since 1998

Editionen mit Sonderbodenbild/ Editions with special backstamp:

Modell-Nr. Model No.	Ausgabejahr Year	Ausgabeland Country	
82/2/0	1998	USA	CE
82/0	1998	QVC, USA	CE

OE: Offene Edition / Open Edition
CE: Produktion beendet / Closed Edition
TWD: Vorübergehend nicht mehr in Produktion / Temporarily withdrawn from production

Modell-Nr. Model No.	Größe / Size cm / inch	Modellierdatum Sculpting Date	
83	14 / 5.50	1938	OE

Editionen mit Sonderbodenbild/ Editions with special backstamp:

Modell-Nr. Model No.	Ausgabejahr Year	Ausgabeland Country	
83	1998	QVC, USA	CE

Hum 83
Fromme Weisen
Angel Serenade With Lamb

Modell-Nr. Model No.	Größe / Size cm / inch	Modellierdatum Sculpting Date	
84/0	13 / 5.25	1938	OE
84/V	32,5 / 12.75	1938	TWD

Editionen mit Sonderbodenbild/ Editions with special backstamp:

Modell-Nr. Model No.	Ausgabejahr Year	Ausgabeland Country	
84/0	1998	QVC, USA	CE

84/0

Hum 84
Am Wegesrand · Worship

Modell-Nr. Model No.	Größe / Size cm / inch	Modellierdatum Sculpting Date	
85/4/0	7,5 / 3.00	1984	CE seit / since 1998
85/0	12,5 / 5.00	1938	OE
85/II	18 / 7.00	1938	TWD seit / since 1998
85/III	32 / 12.5	1997	

Editionen mit Sonderbodenbild/ Editions with special backstamp:

Modell-Nr. Model No.	Ausgabejahr Year	Ausgabeort Country	
85/III	1999	HongKong	CE
85/III	1999	Taiwan	CE

85/0

Hum 85
Ständchen · Serenade

Anmerkung/Note:

85/III Offene Edition ab 2001.

85/III Open Edition 2001.

Hum 86
Wanderlied · Happiness

Modell-Nr. Model No.	Größe / Size cm / inch	Modellierdatum Sculpting Date	
86	12 / 4.75	1938	OE

Editionen mit Sonderbodenbild/ Editions with special backstamp:

Modell-Nr. Model No.	Ausgabejahr Year	Ausgabeort Country	
86	1998	QVC, USA	CE

Hum 87
Für's Vaterle, Rettichbub · For Father

Modell-Nr. Model No.	Größe / Size cm / inch	Modellierdatum Sculpting Date	
87	14 / 5.50	1938	OE

Editionen mit Sonderbodenbild/ Editions with special backstamp:

Modell-Nr. Model No.	Ausgabejahr Year	Ausgabeort Country	
87	1996	QVC, USA	CE
87	1996	"Hummelmuseum" USA	CE
87	1998	QVC, USA	CE

Anmerkung/Note:

Diese Figur kann mit einer persönlichen Widmung beschriftet werden. Fragen Sie Ihren Fachhändler.

This figurine is available in our Personalisation Program with your own personal message. Just ask your local retailer.

88/I

Hum 88
Schutzengel · Heavenly Protection

Modell-Nr. Model No.	Größe / Size cm / inch	Modellierdatum Sculpting Date	
88/I	17 / 6.75	1962	OE
88/II	23 / 9.00	1938	TWD seit / since 1998

Editionen mit Sonderbodenbild/ Editions with special backstamp:

Modell-Nr. Model No.	Ausgabejahr Year	Ausgabeort Country	
88/I	1998	QVC, USA	CE

OE: Offene Edition / Open Edition
CE: Produktion beendet / Closed Edition
TWD: Vorübergehend nicht mehr in Produktion / Temporarily withdrawn from production

Modell-Nr. Model No.	Größe / Size cm / inch	Modellierdatum Sculpting Date	
89/I	13,5 / 5.25	1938	OE
89/II	19 / 7.50	1938	TWD

Editionen mit Sonderbodenbild/ Editions with special backstamp:

Modell-Nr. Model No.	Ausgabejahr Year	Ausgabeort Country	
89/I	1998	"60th Anniversary" Weltweit, Worldwide	CE
89/II	1996	"125 Jahre Goebel" HongKong	CE
89/II	1999	"Caribbean Collection" Karibik	CE

Hum 89
Heimkehr, Baßgeiger · Little Cellist

Anmerkung/Note:

Hum 89/II Expression of Youth. CE seit 1998.

Hum 89/II Expression of Youth. CE since 1998.

Heimkehr, Baßgeiger · Little Cellist
Expression Of Youth

Modell-Nr. Model No.	Größe / Size cm / inch	Modellierdatum Sculpting Date	
90/A	12 / 4.75	1938	CE

Anmerkung/Note:

Kein Verkauf, nur Musterfertigung.

Never distributed, archives samples only.

Hum 90/A
Abendlied · Eventide
Buchstützen · Book Ends

OE: Offene Edition / Open Edition
CE: Produktion beendet / Closed Edition
TWD: Vorübergehend nicht mehr in Produktion / Temporarily withdrawn from production

Modell-Nr. Model No.	Größe / Size cm / inch	Modellierdatum Sculpting Date	
90/B	11 / 4.25	1938	CE

Anmerkung/Note:

Kein Verkauf, nur Musterfertigung.

Never distributed, archives samples only.

Hum 90/B
Bei Mutter Maria · Adoration
Buchstützen · Book Ends

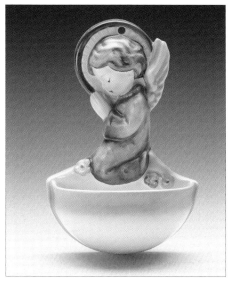

Modell-Nr. Model No.	Größe / Size cm / inch	Modellierdatum Sculpting Date	
91/A	12 / 4.75	1938	OE

Hum 91/A
Engel, links schauend · Angel facing left
Weihkessel · Holy Water Font

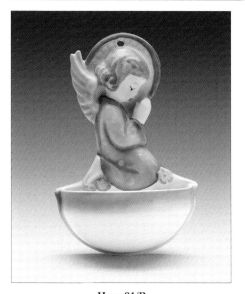

Modell-Nr. Model No.	Größe / Size cm / inch	Modellierdatum Sculpting Date	
91 B	12 / 4.75	1938	OE

Hum 91/B
Engel, rechts schauend · Angel facing right
Weihkessel · Holy Water Font

OE: Offene Edition / Open Edition
CE: Produktion beendet / Closed Edition
TWD: Vorübergehend nicht mehr in Produktion / Temporarily withdrawn from production

Modell-Nr. Model No.	Größe / Size cm / inch	Modellierdatum Sculpting Date	
92	13 x 14 5.25 x 5.50	1938	TWD

Hum 92
Wanderbub · Merry Wanderer
Wandbild · Wall Plaque

Modell-Nr. Model No.	Größe / Size cm / inch	Modellierdatum Sculpting Date	
93	13 x 14 5.25 x 5.50	1938	TWD

Hum 93
Geigerlein · Little Fiddler
Wandbild · Wall Plaque

94/I

Modell-Nr. Model No.	Größe / Size cm / inch	Modellierdatum Sculpting Date	
94/3/0	10 / 4.00	1938	OE
94/I	14 / 5.50	1938	TWD seit / since 1998

Hum 94
Hänsel und Gretel · Surprise

OE: Offene Edition / Open Edition
CE: Produktion beendet / Closed Edition
TWD: Vorübergehend nicht mehr in Produktion / Temporarily withdrawn from production

Modell-Nr. Model No.	Größe / Size cm / inch	Modellierdatum Sculpting Date	
95	14 / 5.50	1938	OE

Editionen mit Sonderbodenbild/ Editions with special backstamp:

Modell-Nr. Model No.	Ausgabejahr Year	Ausgabeort Country	
95	1998	QVC, USA	CE

Hum 95
Dorfheld · Brother

Modell-Nr. Model No.	Größe / Size cm / inch	Modellierdatum Sculpting Date	
96	12 / 4.75	1938	OE

Editionen mit Sonderbodenbild/ Editions with special backstamp:

Modell-Nr. Model No.	Ausgabejahr Year	Ausgabeort Country	
96	1996	QVC, USA	CE

Hum 96
Gretel · Little Shopper

Modell-Nr. Model No.	Größe / Size cm / inch	Modellierdatum Sculpting Date	
97	11.5 / 4.50	1938	OE

Hum 97
Der kleine Musikant · Trumpet Boy

OE: Offene Edition / Open Edition
CE: Produktion beendet / Closed Edition
TWD: Vorübergehend nicht mehr in Produktion / Temporarily withdrawn from production

Modell-Nr. Model No.	Größe / Size cm / inch	Modellierdatum Sculpting Date	
104		1938	CE

Anmerkung/Note:

Kein Verkauf, nur Musterfertigung.

Never distributed, archives samples only.

Keine Archivmuster vorhanden.

No Samples available in our Archives.

Hum 104
Abendlied · Eventide
Tischlampe · Table Lamp

Modell-Nr. Model No.	Größe / Size cm / inch	Modellierdatum Sculpting Date	
105		1938	CE

Anmerkung/Note:

Kein Verkauf, nur Musterfertigung.

Never distributed, archives samples only.

Hum 105
Bei Mutter Maria · Adoration

Modell-Nr. Model No.	Größe / Size cm / inch	Modellierdatum Sculpting Date	
106	13 / 5.25	1938	CE

Anmerkung/Note:

Kein Verkauf, nur Musterfertigung.

Never distributed, archives samples only.

Hum 106
Wanderbub · Merry Wanderer
Wandbild · Wall Plaque

OE: Offene Edition / Open Edition
CE: Produktion beendet / Closed Edition
TWD: Vorübergehend nicht mehr in Produktion / Temporarily withdrawn from production

Modell-Nr. Model No.	Größe / Size cm / inch	Modellierdatum Sculpting Date	
107	12,5 / 5.00	1938	CE

Anmerkung/Note:

Kein Verkauf, nur Musterfertigung.

Never distributed, archives samples only.

Hum 107
Geigerlein · Little Fiddler
Wandbild · Wall Plaque

Modell-Nr. Model No.	Größe / Size cm / inch	Modellierdatum Sculpting Date	
108	26 / 10.25	1938	CE

Anmerkung/Note:

Kein Verkauf, nur Musterfertigung.

Never distributed, archives samples only.

Hum 108
Schutzengel mit 2 Kindern
Angel with two children at feet
Wandfigur · Wall figurine

Modell-Nr. Model No.	Größe / Size cm / inch	Modellierdatum Sculpting Date	
109/0	13 / 5.25	1938	OE
109/II	19,5 / 7.75	1938	CE

Editionen mit Sonderbodenbild/ Editions with special backstamp:

Modell-Nr. Model No.	Ausgabejahr Year	Ausgabeort Country	
109/0	1999	"Glow Of Freedom" Militär, Military	CE

Hum 109
Hinaus in die Ferne · Happy Traveller

OE: Offene Edition / Open Edition
CE: Produktion beendet / Closed Edition
TWD: Vorübergehend nicht mehr in Produktion / Temporarily withdrawn from production

Modell-Nr. Model No.	Größe / Size cm / inch	Modellierdatum Sculpting Date	
110/0	8 / 3.25	1938	OE
110/I	9 / 3.50	1938	OE
III/110	15 / 6.00	1939	TWD

Hum 110
Heini, Bandoneonspieler · Let's Sing

Editionen mit Sonderbodenbild/ Editions with special backstamp:

Modell-Nr. Model No.	Ausgabejahr Year	Ausgabeort Country	
110/0	1999	"60th Anniversary"	CE
110/I		Weltweit, Worldwide	

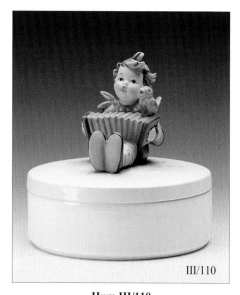

Hum III/110
Heini, Bandoneonspieler · Let's Sing
Dose · Box

Hum 111
Vaters G'scheitester · Wayside Harmony

Modell-Nr. Model No.	Größe / Size cm / inch	Modellierdatum Sculpting Date	
111/3/0	10 / 4.00	1938	OE
111/I	13 / 5.25	1938	TWD seit / since 1998

Editionen mit Sonderbodenbild/ Editions with special backstamp:

Modell-Nr. Model No.	Ausgabejahr Year	Ausgabeort Country	
111/3/0	1999	"Kloster Neustift" Italien, Italy	CE
111/3/0		USA	CE
111/I		USA	CE

Anmerkung/Note:

Tischlampe Nr. II/111 wurde geändert in Nr. 224/I.

Table Lamp No. II/111 changed to No. 224/I.

Modell-Nr. Model No.	Größe / Size cm / inch	Modellierdatum Sculpting Date	
112/3/0	10 / 4.00	1938	OE
112/I	12,5 / 5.00	1938	TWD seit / since 1998

Editionen mit Sonderbodenbild/ Editions with special backstamp:

Modell-Nr. Model No.	Ausgabejahr Year	Ausgabeort Country	
112/3/0		USA	CE
112/I		USA	CE

Anmerkung/Note:

Tischlampe Nr. II/112 wurde geändert in Nr. 225/I.

Table Lamp No. II/112 changed to No. 225/I.

Hum 112
Mutters Liebste · Just Resting

Modell-Nr. Model No.	Größe / Size cm / inch	Modellierdatum Sculpting Date	
113	9 / 3.50		CE

Hum 113
Adventsgruppe · Heavenly Song
Kerzenhalter · Candle Holder

Modell-Nr. Model No.	Größe / Size cm / inch	Modellierdatum Sculpting Date	
114	9 / 3.50	1938	TWD

Hum 114
Heini · Let's Sing
Aschenbecher · Ashtray

OE: Offene Edition / Open Edition
CE: Produktion beendet / Closed Edition
TWD: Vorübergehend nicht mehr in Produktion / Temporarily withdrawn from production

Modell-Nr. Model No.	Größe / Size cm / inch	Modellierdatum Sculpting Date	
115	9 / 3.50	1939	OE

Sonderversion / Special Edition

Modell-Nr. Model No.	Ausgabejahr Year	Ausgabeort Country	
115	1992	USA	CE

Anmerkung/Note:

Kerzenhalter.

Candle Holder.

Hum 115
Mädchen mit Blumenstrauß
Girl With Nosegay

Modell-Nr. Model No.	Größe / Size cm / inch	Modellierdatum Sculpting Date	
116	9 / 3.50	1939	OE

Sonderversion / Special Edition

Modell-Nr. Model No.	Ausgabejahr Year	Ausgabeort Country	
116	1992	USA	CE

Anmerkung/Note:

Kerzenhalter.

Candle Holder.

Hum 116
Mädchen mit Tannenbaum
Girl With Fir Tree

Modell-Nr. Model No.	Größe / Size cm / inch	Modellierdatum Sculpting Date	
117	9 / 3.50	1939	OE

Sonderversion / Special Edition

Modell-Nr. Model No.	Ausgabejahr Year	Ausgabeort Country	
117	1992	USA	CE

Anmerkung/Note:

Kerzenhalter.

Candle Holder.

Hum 117
Junge mit Holzpferd
Boy With Horse

OE: Offene Edition / Open Edition
CE: Produktion beendet / Closed Edition
TWD: Vorübergehend nicht mehr in Produktion / Temporarily withdrawn from production

Modell-Nr. Model No.	Größe / Size cm / inch	Modellierdatum Sculpting Date	
118	13 / 5.25	1939	OE

Editionen mit Sonderbodenbild/ Editions with special backstamp:

Modell-Nr. Model No.	Ausgabejahr Year	Ausgabeort Country	
118	1990	mit DDR Pfennig, with GDR coin, USA	CE

Hum 118
Sparhummelchen · Little Thrifty

Modell-Nr. Model No.	Größe / Size cm / inch	Modellierdatum Sculpting Date	
119/2/0	11 / 4.25	1985	OE
119/0	13 / 5.25	1939	OE

Editionen mit Sonderbodenbild/ Editions with special backstamp:

Modell-Nr. Model No.	Ausgabejahr Year	Ausgabeort Country	
119/2/0	1996	USA	CE
119/0	1998	USA	CE

119/0

Hum 119
Eilbote · Postman

Modell-Nr. Model No.	Größe / Size cm / inch	Modellierdatum Sculpting Date		
120/A	–	1939	CE	Gesangsprobe, Joyful
120/B	–	1939	CE	Heini, Bandoneonspieler, Let's Sing

Anmerkung/Note:

Kein Verkauf, nur Musterfertigung.

Never distributed, archives samples only.

Keine Archivmuster vorhanden.

No Samples available in our Archives.

Hum 120
Buchstützen · Book Ends

OE: Offene Edition / Open Edition
CE: Produktion beendet / Closed Edition
TWD: Vorübergehend nicht mehr in Produktion / Temporarily withdrawn from production

Hum 121
Buchstützen · Book Ends

Modell-Nr. Model No.	Größe / Size cm / inch	Modellierdatum Sculpting Date		
121/A	–	1939	CE	Vaters G'scheitester, Wayside Harmony
121/B	–	1939	CE	Mutters Liebste, Just Resting

Anmerkung/Note:

Kein Verkauf, nur Musterfertigung.

Never distributed, archives samples only.

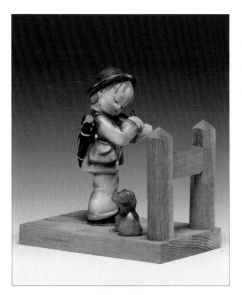

Hum 122
Buchstützen · Book Ends

Modell-Nr. Model No.	Größe / Size cm / inch	Modellierdatum Sculpting Date		
122/A	13,5 / 5.50	1939	CE	Geigerlein, Puppy Love
122/B	13 / 5.25	1939	CE	Ständchen, Serenade

Anmerkung/Note:

Kein Verkauf, nur Musterfertigung.

Never distributed, archives samples only.

Hum 123
Max und Moritz · Max And Moritz

Modell-Nr. Model No.	Größe / Size cm / inch	Modellierdatum Sculpting Date	
123	13 / 5.25	1939	OE

OE: Offene Edition / Open Edition
CE: Produktion beendet / Closed Edition
TWD: Vorübergehend nicht mehr in Produktion / Temporarily withdrawn from production

Modell-Nr. Model No.	Größe / Size cm / inch	Modellierdatum Sculpting Date	
124/0	15 / 6.00	1939	OE
124/I	16,5 / 6.50	1939	OE

Anmerkung/Note:

Letzte Ausgabe 2001, Sonderbodenbild und Plombe im letzten Produktionsjahr.

Final Issue 2001, special backstamp and medallion in the last year of production.

Farbvariationen bei alten Figuren: grauer Mantel, graue Hose, rosa Weste oder brauner Mantel, grüne Hosen, rosa Weste.

Color variations on old figurines: grey coat, grey trousers, pink vest or brown coat, green trousers, pink vest.

Hum 124
Chef · Hello

Modell-Nr. Model No.	Größe / Size cm / inch	Modellierdatum Sculpting Date	
125	10 x 12	1939	TWD
	4.00 x 4.75		

Hum 125
Ferienfreude · Vacation-Time
Wandbild · Wall Plaque

Modell-Nr. Model No.	Größe / Size cm / inch	Modellierdatum Sculpting Date	
126	12 x 12	1939	TWD
	4.75 x 4.75		

Hum 126
Angsthase · Retreat To Safety
Wandbild · Wall Plaque

OE: Offene Edition / Open Edition
CE: Produktion beendet / Closed Edition
TWD: Vorübergehend nicht mehr in Produktion / Temporarily withdrawn from production

Modell-Nr. Model No.	Größe / Size cm / inch	Modellierdatum Sculpting Date	
133	12 / 4.75	1939	OE

Hum 133
Mutters Stütze · Mother's Helper

Modell-Nr. Model No.	Größe / Size cm / inch	Modellierdatum Sculpting Date	
134	15 x 15 6.00 x 6.00	1939	TWD

Hum 134
Das Quartett · Quartet
Wandbild · Wall Plaque

Modell-Nr. Model No.	Größe / Size cm / inch	Modellierdatum Sculpting Date	
135/5/0	7 / 2.75	1991	CE
135/4/0	7,5 / 3.00	1984	CE seit / since 1998
135/0	12 / 4.75	1940	OE
135/III	30 / 11.75	1997	OE ab 2001, OE 2001

Editionen mit Sonderbodenbild / Editions with special backstamp:

Modell-Nr. Model No.	Ausgabejahr Year	Ausgabeort Country	
135/5/0	1998	„Pen Pals" USA	CE
135/0	1999	"Bronner's Christmas Wonderland"	CE
		USA	CE
135/III	1998	HongKong	CE
135/III	1998	Taiwan	CE

135/0

Hum 135
Heldentenor · Soloist

Hum 136
Gute Freunde · Friends

Modell-Nr. Model No.	Größe / Size cm / inch	Modellierdatum Sculpting Date	
136/I	13 / 5.25	1953	OE
136/V	28 / 11.00	1940	TWD seit / since 1998

Editionen mit Sonderbodenbild/ Editions with special backstamp:

Modell-Nr. Model No.	Ausgabejahr Year	Ausgabeort Country	
136/I	1999	"Commemorative Edition" USA	CE

Anmerkung/Note:

136/V geringe Stückzahlen aus rotbraunem Terracotta wurden produziert.

Sold at one time in reddish-brown terra cotta finish.

Hum 137
Kind im Bettchen · Child In Bed
Wandbild · Wall Plaque

Modell-Nr. Model No.	Größe / Size cm / inch	Modellierdatum Sculpting Date	
137	7 / 2.75	1940	TWD seit / since 1998

Hum 138
Baby in Wiege · Tiny Baby in crib
Wandbild · Wall Plaque

Modell-Nr. Model No.	Größe / Size cm / inch	Modellierdatum Sculpting Date	
138	7,5 / 3.00	1940	CE

Anmerkung/Note:

Kein Verkauf, nur Musterfertigung.

Never distributed, archives samples only.

OE: Offene Edition / Open Edition
CE: Produktion beendet / Closed Edition
TWD: Vorübergehend nicht mehr in Produktion / Temporarily withdrawn from production

Modell-Nr. Model No.	Größe / Size cm / inch	Modellierdatum Sculpting Date	
139	6,5 / 2.50	1940	TWD seit / since 1998

Hum 139
Sitzendes Kind mit Schmetterling
Flitting Butterfly
Wandbild · Wall Plaque

Modell-Nr. Model No.	Größe / Size cm / inch	Modellierdatum Sculpting Date	
140	11 x 16	1940	TWD
	4.25 x 6.25		

Hum 140
Trara, die Post ist da · The Mail Is Here
Wandbild · Wall Plaque

141/I

Modell-Nr. Model No.	Größe / Size cm / inch	Modellierdatum Sculpting Date	
141/3/0	11 / 4.25	1940	OE
141/I	15 / 6.00	1940	OE
141/V	27 / 10.75	1968	OE
141/X	84 / 33.00	1975	OE

Hum 141
Frühling · Apple Tree Girl

OE: Offene Edition / Open Edition
CE: Produktion beendet / Closed Edition
TWD: Vorübergehend nicht mehr in Produktion / Temporarily withdrawn from production

141/3/0

Hum 141
Frühling · Apple Tree Girl

Editionen mit Sonderbodenbild/ Editions with special backstamp:

Modell-Nr. Model No.	Ausgabejahr Year	Ausgabeort Country	
141/3/0	2000	Kanada, Canada	OE
141/I	1999	"Caribbean Collection" Karibik	CE

142/I

Hum 142
Herbst · Apple Tree Boy

Modell-Nr. Model No.	Größe / Size cm / inch	Modellierdatum Sculpting Date	
142/3/0	11 / 4.25	1940	OE
142/I	15 / 6.00	1940	OE
142/V	27 / 10.75	1968	OE
142/X	84 / 33.00	1975	OE

142/3/0

Hum 142
Herbst · Apple Tree Boy

Editionen mit Sonderbodenbild/ Editions with special backstamp:

Modell-Nr. Model No.	Ausgabejahr Year	Ausgabeort Country	
142/3/0	2000	Kanada, Canada	OE

OE: Offene Edition / Open Edition
CE: Produktion beendet / Closed Edition
TWD: Vorübergehend nicht mehr in Produktion / Temporarily withdrawn from production

Modell-Nr. Model No.	Größe / Size cm / inch	Modellierdatum Sculpting Date	
143/0	13 / 5.25	1940	CE
143/I	17 / 6.75	1940	CE

Anmerkung/Note:

143/0, 143/I Letzte Ausgabe 1998, Sonderbodenbild und Plombe im letzten Produktionsjahr.

Final Issue 1998, special backstamp and medallion in the last year of production.

Hum 143
Meister Wichtig · Boots

Modell-Nr. Model No.	Größe / Size cm / inch	Modellierdatum Sculpting Date	
144	10 / 4.00	1941	OE

Hum 144
Singendes Kind mit Engelein
Angelic Song

Modell-Nr. Model No.	Größe / Size cm / inch	Modellierdatum Sculpting Date	
145	9,5 / 3.75	1941	OE

Hum 145
Betendes Kind mit Engelein
Little Guardian

OE: Offene Edition / Open Edition
CE: Produktion beendet / Closed Edition
TWD: Vorübergehend nicht mehr in Produktion / Temporarily withdrawn from production

Modell-Nr. Model No.	Größe / Size cm / inch	Modellierdatum Sculpting Date	
146	12 / 4.75	1941	TWD

Hum 146
Engelgrüppchen · Angel Duet
Weihkessel · Holy Water Font

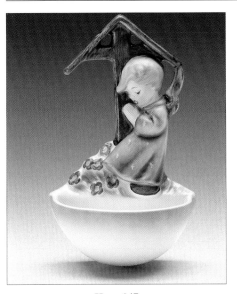

Modell-Nr. Model No.	Größe / Size cm / inch	Modellierdatum Sculpting Date	
147	13 / 5.25	1941	OE

Hum 147
Engel · Angel Shrine
Weihkessel · Holy Water Font

150/0

Modell-Nr. Model No.	Größe / Size cm / inch	Modellierdatum Sculpting Date	
150/2/0	11 / 4.25	1942	OE
150/0	13,5 / 5.25	1942	TWD seit / since 1998
150/I	16 / 6.25	1942	TWD seit / since 1998

Hum 150
Hausmusik · Happy Days

OE: Offene Edition / Open Edition
CE: Produktion beendet / Closed Edition
TWD: Vorübergehend nicht mehr in Produktion / Temporarily withdrawn from production

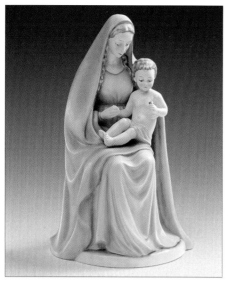

Modell-Nr. Model No.	Größe / Size cm / inch	Modellierdatum Sculpting Date	
151	30,5 / 12.00	1942	TWD

Hum 151
sitzende Madonna mit Kind
Madonna holding child

Anmerkung/Note:

Ohne Dekoration oder mit Umhang in den Farben hellblau, dunkelblau, braun oder elfenbein.

Without decoration or with pastel blue, dark blue, brown or ivory coat.

Modell-Nr. Model No.	Größe / Size cm / inch	Modellierdatum Sculpting Date	
152/A/0	13 / 5.25	1954	OE
152/A/II	19 / 7.50	1942	OE

152/A/0

Hum 152/A
Geborgen (Junge) · Umbrella Boy

152/B/0

Hum 152/B
Geborgen (Mädchen) · Umbrella Girl

Modell-Nr. Model No.	Größe / Size cm / inch	Modellierdatum Sculpting Date	
152/B/0	13 / 5.25	1949	OE
152/B/II	19 / 7.50	1949	OE

OE: Offene Edition / Open Edition
CE: Produktion beendet / Closed Edition
TWD: Vorübergehend nicht mehr in Produktion / Temporarily withdrawn from production

Hum 153
Auf Wiedersehen · Auf Wiedersehen

153/I

Modell-Nr. Model No.	Größe / Size cm / inch	Modellierdatum Sculpting Date	
153/0	14 / 5.50	1943	CE
153/I	17 / 6.75	1943	CE

Sonderausgabe "Luftbrücke Berlin" 1993
Zur Erinnerung an die "Berliner Luftbrücke"- einem beispiellosen
Kampf für den Freiheitswillen der Menschen
Auf 25.000 Stück weltweit limitiert und einzeln nummeriert.
Produktion beendet.
21 x 23 x 16,5 cm

Commemorative Edition "Berlin Airlift" 1993
Commemorative Edition to honor the Berlin Airlift - a heroic effort to
keep a city free.
Worldwide limited and numbered edition of 25,000 pcs.
Closed Edition.
8.25 x 9.00 x 6.50 inch

Anmerkung/Note:

Letzte Ausgabe 2000, Sonderbodenbild und Plombe im letzten Produktionsjahr.

Final Issue 2000, special backstamp and medallion in the last year of production.

Hum 154
Herr Ober · Waiter

154/I

Modell-Nr. Model No.	Größe / Size cm / inch	Modellierdatum Sculpting Date	
154/0	15 / 6.00	1943	OE
154/I	17 / 6.75	1943	TWD seit / since 1998

Editionen mit Sonderbodenbild/ Editions with special backstamp:

Modell-Nr. Model No.	Ausgabejahr Year	Ausgabeort Country	
154/0	1995	"Kremsmünster" Österreich, Austria	CE
154/0	1996	"Blue Nun" USA	CE
154/I	1995	"Kremsmünster" Österreich, Austria	CE

Hum 157

Hum 158

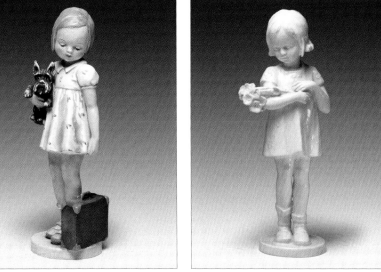

Hum 159

Hum 160

Hum 161

Modell-Nr. Model No.	Größe / Size cm / inch	Modellierdatum Sculpting Date	
157	28 / 11.00	1943	CE
158	28,5 / 11.25	1943	CE
159	27,5 / 10.75	1943	CE
160	33 / 13.00	1943	CE
161	26 / 10.25	1943	CE

Anmerkung/Note:

Vom Kloster Sießen nicht genehmigt. Kein Verkauf, nur Musterfertigung.

Not approved by the Convent of Siessen. Never distributed, archives samples only.

Hum 163
Glockenturm mit Engeln · Whitsuntide

Modell-Nr. Model No.	Größe / Size cm / inch	Modellierdatum Sculpting Date	
163	17 / 6.75	1946	TWD seit / since 1998

OE: Offene Edition / Open Edition
CE: Produktion beendet / Closed Edition
TWD: Vorübergehend nicht mehr in Produktion / Temporarily withdrawn from production

Modell-Nr. Model No.	Größe / Size cm / inch	Modellierdatum Sculpting Date	
164	12 / 4.75	1946	OE

Hum 164
Am Wegesrand · Worship
Weihkessel · Holy Water Font

Modell-Nr. Model No.	Größe / Size cm / inch	Modellierdatum Sculpting Date	
165	13,5 x 13,5	1948	TWD
	5.25 x 5.25		

Hum 165
Kind mit Hängematte · Swaying Lullaby
Wandbild · Wall Plaque

Modell-Nr. Model No.	Größe / Size cm / inch	Modellierdatum Sculpting Date	
166	9 x 16	1946	TWD
	3.50 x 6.25		

Hum 166
Junge mit Vogel · Boy With Bird
Aschenbecher · Ashtray

OE: Offene Edition / Open Edition
CE: Produktion beendet / Closed Edition
TWD: Vorübergehend nicht mehr in Produktion / Temporarily withdrawn from production

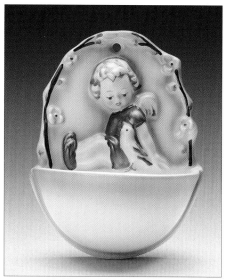

Modell-Nr. Model No.	Größe / Size cm / inch	Modellierdatum Sculpting Date	
167	12 / 4.75	1945	OE

Hum 167
Sitzender Engel · Angel With Bird
Weihkessel · Holy Water Font

Modell-Nr. Model No.	Größe / Size cm / inch	Modellierdatum Sculpting Date	
168	14,5 x 14,5 5.75 x 5.75	1948	TWD

Hum 168
Stehender Junge mit Herz · Standing Boy
Wandbild · Wall Plaque

Modell-Nr. Model No.	Größe / Size cm / inch	Modellierdatum Sculpting Date	
169	10 / 4.00	1945	OE

Hum 169
Frühlingslied · Bird Duet

Anmerkung/Note:

Diese Figur kann mit einer persönlichen Widmung beschriftet werden. Fragen Sie Ihren Fachhändler.

This figurine is available in our Personalisation Program with your own personal message. Just ask your local retailer.

Modell-Nr. Model No.	Größe / Size cm / inch	Modellierdatum Sculpting Date	
170/I	18,5 / 7.25	1961	OE
170/III	25 / 9.75	1943	CE

Hum 170
Schwieriges Problem · School Boys

Modell-Nr. Model No.	Größe / Size cm / inch	Modellierdatum Sculpting Date	
171/4/0	8 / 3.25	1986	CE seit / since 1998
171/0	11 / 4.25	1944	OE

Editionen mit Sonderbodenbild/ Editions with special backstamp:

Modell-Nr. Model No.	Ausgabejahr Year	Ausgabeland Country	
171/0	1999	USA	CE

Hum 171
Kehrliesl · Little Sweeper

Modell-Nr. Model No.	Größe / Size cm / inch	Modellierdatum Sculpting Date	
172/4/0	8 / 3.25	1990	CE seit / since 1998
172/0	20 / 8.00	1961	TWD seit / since 1998
172/II	27,5 / 10.75	1947	CE seit / since 1998

Anmerkung/Note:

Hum 172/4/0, Erstausgabe 1994 mit Sonderbodenbild.

First Issue 1994 with special decal.

Hum 172
Adventsengel mit Mandoline
Festival Harmony (Mandolin)

OE: Offene Edition / Open Edition
CE: Produktion beendet / Closed Edition
TWD: Vorübergehend nicht mehr in Produktion / Temporarily withdrawn from production

Modell-Nr. Model No.	Größe / Size cm / inch	Modellierdatum Sculpting Date	
173/4/0	8 / 3.25	1990	CE seit / since 1998
173/0	20 / 8.00	1961	TWD seit / since 1998
173/II	27,5 / 10.75	1947	CE seit / since 1998

173/0

Hum 173
Adventsengel mit Flöte
Festival Harmony (Flute)

Anmerkung/Note:

Hum 173/4/0, Erstausgabe 1995 mit Sonderbodenbild.

First Issue 1995 with special backstamp.

173/4/0

Modell-Nr. Model No.	Größe / Size cm / inch	Modellierdatum Sculpting Date	
174	11 / 4.25	1945	OE

Editionen mit Sonderbodenbild/ Editions with special backstamp:

Modell-Nr. Model No.	Ausgabejahr Year	Ausgabeland Country	
174	1999	USA	CE

Hum 174
Liebt mich, liebt mich nicht...
She Loves Me, She Loves Me Not...

Modell-Nr. Model No.	Größe / Size cm / inch	Modellierdatum Sculpting Date	
175	14 / 5.50	1945	CE

Anmerkung/Note:

Letzte Ausgabe 1997, Sonderbodenbild und Plombe im letzten Produktionsjahr.

Final Issue 1997, special backstamp and medallion in the last year of production.

Hum 175
Markt-Christl · Mother's Darling

OE:	Offene Edition / Open Edition
CE:	Produktion beendet / Closed Edition
TWD:	Vorübergehend nicht mehr in Produktion / Temporarily withdrawn from production

Hum 176
Gratulanten · Happy Birthday

Modell-Nr. Model No.	Größe / Size cm / inch	Modellierdatum Sculpting Date	
176/0	13 / 5.25	1945	OE
176/I	15 / 6.00	1945	TWD seit / since 1998

Editionen mit Sonderbodenbild/ Editions with special backstamp:

Modell-Nr. Model No.	Ausgabejahr Year	Ausgabeland Country	
176/0	1999	"90th Anniversary" Deutschland / Germany	CE
176/0	1999	USA	CE

Hum 177
's Meisterstück · School Girls

Modell-Nr. Model No.	Größe / Size cm / inch	Modellierdatum Sculpting Date	
177/I	19 / 7.50	1961	OE
177/III	24,5 / 9.50	1946	CE

Editionen mit Sonderbodenbild/ Editions with special backstamp:

Modell-Nr. Model No.	Ausgabejahr Year	Ausgabeland Country	
177/I	2000	Schweden / Sweden	CE

Hum 178
Der Fotograf · The Photographer

Modell-Nr. Model No.	Größe / Size cm / inch	Modellierdatum Sculpting Date	
178	12 / 4.75	1948	OE

Editionen mit Sonderbodenbild/ Editions with special backstamp:

Modell-Nr. Model No.	Ausgabejahr Year	Ausgabeland Country	
178	1999	USA	CE

OE: Offene Edition / Open Edition
CE: Produktion beendet / Closed Edition
TWD: Vorübergehend nicht mehr in Produktion / Temporarily withdrawn from production

Modell-Nr. Model No.	Größe / Size cm / inch	Modellierdatum Sculpting Date	
179	13 / 5.25	1946	TWD seit / since 1998

Hum 179
Zaungäste · Coquettes

Modell-Nr. Model No.	Größe / Size cm / inch	Modellierdatum Sculpting Date	
180	13 x 12 / 5.25 x 4.75	1946	TWD

Hum 180
Sitzendes Kind mit Trompete
Tuneful Good Nigh
Wandbild · Wall Plaque

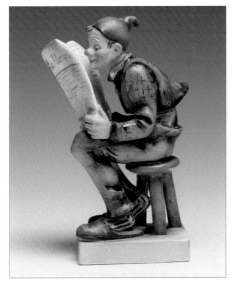

Modell-Nr. Model No.	Größe / Size cm / inch	Modellierdatum Sculpting Date	
181	16 / 6.25	1948	CE

Anmerkung/Note:

Vom Kloster Sießen nicht genehmigt. Kein Verkauf, nur Musterfertigung.

Not approved by the Convent of Siessen. Never distributed, archives samples only.

Hum 181
Alter Mann mit Zeitung
Old Man with Newspaper

OE: Offene Edition / Open Edition
CE: Produktion beendet / Closed Edition
TWD: Vorübergehend nicht mehr in Produktion / Temporarily withdrawn from production

Modell-Nr. Model No.	Größe / Size cm / inch	Modellierdatum Sculpting Date	
182	11 / 4.25	1946	OE

Editionen mit Sonderbodenbild/ Editions with special backstamp:

Modell-Nr. Model No.	Ausgabejahr Year	Ausgabeland Country	
182	2001	"50th Anniversary" USA	OE

Hum 182
Freunde · Good Friends

Modell-Nr. Model No.	Größe / Size cm / inch	Modellierdatum Sculpting Date	
183	23 / 9.00	1946	TWD seit / since 1998

Hum 183
Waldandacht, Marterl · Forest Shrine

Modell-Nr. Model No.	Größe / Size cm / inch	Modellierdatum Sculpting Date	
184	13,5 / 5.25	1946	OE

Hum 184
Das Allerneueste · Latest News

OE: Offene Edition / Open Edition
CE: Produktion beendet / Closed Edition
TWD: Vorübergehend nicht mehr in Produktion / Temporarily withdrawn from production

Das Allerneueste · Latest News
Personalisierungsprogramm
Personalisation Program

Anmerkung/Note:

Diese Figur kann mit einer persönlichen Widmung beschriftet werden. Fragen Sie Ihren Fachhändler.

This figurine is available in our Personalisation Program with your own personal message. Just ask your local retailer.

Editionen mit Sonderbodenbild/ Editions with special backstamp:

Modell-Nr. Model No.	Ausgabejahr Year	Ausgabeland Country	
184	1996	Personalisierungsprogramm Personalisation Program	OE
184	1994	"Bermuda News" Karibik, Caribbean	CE
184	1995	"Bahamas News" Karibik, Caribbean	CE
184	1995	"Island News" Karibik, Caribbean	CE
184	1995	"Cayman News" Karibik, Caribbean	CE
184	1996	"The Stars And Stripes" US Militär, US Military	CE
184	1996	"Frankfurter Sammlerbörse" Deutschland / Germany	CE
184	1996	"New Braunfels Herald" USA	CE
184	1996	"Rüdesheimer Nachrichten" Deutschland / Germany	CE
184	1996	"Milwaukee Journal Sentinel" USA	CE
184	1996	"Latest News" Karibik, Caribbean	CE
184	1997	"Presse Gazette" USA	CE
184	1997	"Goebel Gazette" USA	CE
184	1997	"Rosemont Times" USA	CE
184	1997	"Chicago Times" USA	CE
184	1997	"Jamaica News" Karibik, Caribbean	CE
184	1998	"The Denver Post" USA	CE
184	1998	"The Detroit Post" USA	CE
184	1998	"Cobourg Daily Star" Kanada	CE
184	1998	"St. Louis Post Dispatch" USA	CE
184	1998	"Ramstein" US Militär, US Military	CE
184	1998	"Heidelberg" US Militär, US Military	CE
184	1999	"Daily News" USA	CE
184	1999	"The Denver Post" USA	CE
184	1999	USA	CE
184	2000	USA	CE

OE: Offene Edition / Open Edition
CE: Produktion beendet / Closed Edition
TWD: Vorübergehend nicht mehr in Produktion / Temporarily withdrawn from production

Modell-Nr. Model No.	Größe / Size cm / inch	Modellierdatum Sculpting Date	
185	13 / 5.25	1947	CE

Hum 185
Bandoneonspieler · Accordion Boy

Anmerkung/Note:

Letzte Ausgabe 1994, Sonderbodenbild und Plombe im letzten Produktionsjahr.

Final Issue 1994, special backstamp and medallion in the last year of production.

186/I

Modell-Nr. Model No.	Größe / Size cm / inch	Modellierdatum Sculpting Date	
186/I	13 / 5.25	1947	OE
186/III	33 / 13.00	1997	

Editionen mit Sonderbodenbild/ Editions with special backstamp:

Modell-Nr. Model No.	Ausgabejahr Year	Ausgabeland Country	
186/I	1998	USA	CE
186/I	2001	"50th Anniversary" USA	OE
186/III	1999	HongKong	CE
186/III	1999	Taiwan	CE

Anmerkung/Note:

186/III Offene Edition ab 2002.

186/III Open Edition 2002.

Hum 186
Zum Tanz, Baßgeiger · Sweet Music

Modell-Nr. Model No.	Größe / Size cm / inch	Modellierdatum Sculpting Date		
187	14 x 10	1947	CE	Nur für autorisierte Fachhändler
	5.50 x 4.00			Only available for authorized dealers

Editionen mit Sonderbodenbild/ Editions with special backstamp:

Modell-Nr. Model No.	Ausgabejahr Year	Ausgabeland Country	
187	1997	"Miller's Expo" USA	CE
187	1997	Deutschland, Germany	CE
187	1995	"Celebrating AAFES"	CE
		US Militär, US Military	
187	1997	USA	CE

Hum 187
Händlerschild · Retailer Plaque

OE: Offene Edition / Open Edition
CE: Produktion beendet / Closed Edition
TWD: Vorübergehend nicht mehr in Produktion / Temporarily withdrawn from production

Modell-Nr. Model No.	Größe / Size cm / inch	Modellierdatum Sculpting Date	
188/4/0	8 / 3.25	1990	OE
188/0	14 / 5.50	1982	OE
188/I	18 / 7.00	1948	TWD

Editionen mit Sonderbodenbild/ Editions with special backstamp:

Modell-Nr. Model No.	Ausgabejahr Year	Ausgabeland Country	
188/I	2001	"50th Anniversary" USA	OE

188/I

Hum 188
Himmlische Klänge · Celestial Musician

Anmerkung/Note:

188/4/0 Erste Ausgabe 1993 mit Sonderbodenbild im ersten Produktionsjahr.

First Issue 1993 with special backstamp in the first year of production.

Hum 189
Oma strickend
Old Woman Knitting

Hum 190
Oma, zum Markt gehend
Old Woman Walking To Market

Hum 191
Opa, zum Markt gehend
Old Man Walking To Market

Modell-Nr. Model No.	Größe / Size cm / inch	Modellierdatum Sculpting Date	
189	17 / 6.75	1948	CE
190	17 / 6.75	1948	CE
191	17,5 / 7.00	1948	CE

Anmerkung/Note:

Vom Kloster Sießen nicht genehmigt. Kein Verkauf, nur Musterfertigung.

Not approved by the Convent of Siessen. Never distributed, archives samples only.

OE: Offene Edition / Open Edition
CE: Produktion beendet / Closed Edition
TWD: Vorübergehend nicht mehr in Produktion / Temporarily withdrawn from production

Hum 192
Engel mit Kerze · Candlelight
Kerzenhalter · Candle Holder

Modell-Nr. Model No.	Größe / Size cm / inch	Modellierdatum Sculpting Date	
192	17 / 6.75	1948	TWD seit / since 1998

Anmerkung/Note:

Ältere Figuren mit großer, roter Kerze aus Keramik.

Originally modeled with a long red ceramic candle.

Hum 193
Stille Nachte, Engelgrüppchen · Angel Duet
Kerzenhalter · Candle Holder

Modell-Nr. Model No.	Größe / Size cm / inch	Modellierdatum Sculpting Date	
193	13 / 5.25	1948	TWD seit / since 1998

Hum 194
Engel an der Krippe · Watchful Angel

Modell-Nr. Model No.	Größe / Size cm / inch	Modellierdatum Sculpting Date	
194	16,5 / 6.50	1948	OE

OE: Offene Edition / Open Edition
CE: Produktion beendet / Closed Edition
TWD: Vorübergehend nicht mehr in Produktion / Temporarily withdrawn from production

Modell-Nr. Model No.	Größe / Size cm / inch	Modellierdatum Sculpting Date	
195/2/0	10 / 4.00	1952	OE
195/I	14 / 5.50	1948	TWD seit / since 1998

Hum 195
Angsthase · Barnyard Hero

Editionen mit Sonderbodenbild/ Editions with special backstamp:

Modell-Nr. Model No.	Ausgabejahr Year	Ausgabeland Country	
195/I	2001	"50th Anniversary" USA	OE

Modell-Nr. Model No.	Größe / Size cm / inch	Modellierdatum Sculpting Date	
196/0	13,5 / 5.25	1948	OE
196/I	16,5 / 6.50	1948	TWD

Hum 196
Das Geheimnis · Telling Her Secret

Editionen mit Sonderbodenbild/ Editions with special backstamp:

Modell-Nr. Model No.	Ausgabejahr Year	Ausgabeland Country	
196/0	2001	"50th Anniversary" weltweit, worldwide	OE

Modell-Nr. Model No.	Größe / Size cm / inch	Modellierdatum Sculpting Date	
197/2/0	11 / 4.25	1952	OE
197/I	15 / 6.00	1948	TWD seit / since 1998

Hum 197
Entenmütterchen · Be Patient

Editionen mit Sonderbodenbild/ Editions with special backstamp:

Modell-Nr. Model No.	Ausgabejahr Year	Ausgabeland Country	
197/I	2001	"50th Anniversary" USA	OE

OE: Offene Edition / Open Edition
CE: Produktion beendet / Closed Edition
TWD: Vorübergehend nicht mehr in Produktion / Temporarily withdrawn from production

Hum 198
Glückskauf · Home From Market

Modell-Nr. Model No.	Größe / Size cm / inch	Modellierdatum Sculpting Date	
198/2/0	12 / 4.75	1952	OE
198/I	13,5 / 5.25	1948	TWD seit / since 1998

Editionen mit Sonderbodenbild/ Editions with special backstamp:

Modell-Nr. Model No.	Ausgabejahr Year	Ausgabeland Country	
198/I	2001	"50th Anniversary" USA	OE

Hum 199
Im Hühnerhof · Feeding Time

Modell-Nr. Model No.	Größe / Size cm / inch	Modellierdatum Sculpting Date	
199/0	12 / 4.75	1955	OE
199/I	14 / 5.50	1948	OE

Editionen mit Sonderbodenbild/ Editions with special backstamp:

Modell-Nr. Model No.	Ausgabejahr Year	Ausgabeland Country	
199/I	2001	"50th Anniversary" USA	OE

Hum 200
Ziegenbub · Little Goat Herder

Modell-Nr. Model No.	Größe / Size cm / inch	Modellierdatum Sculpting Date	
200/0	12 / 4.75	1952	OE
200/I	13 / 5.25	1948	OE

Editionen mit Sonderbodenbild/ Editions with special backstamp:

Modell-Nr. Model No.	Ausgabejahr Year	Ausgabeland Country	
200/I	2001	"50th Anniversary" USA	OE

OE: Offene Edition / Open Edition
CE: Produktion beendet / Closed Edition
TWD: Vorübergehend nicht mehr in Produktion / Temporarily withdrawn from production

Modell-Nr. Model No.	Größe / Size cm / inch	Modellierdatum Sculpting Date	
201/2/0	10 / 4.00	1955	OE
201/I	14 / 5.50	1948	TWD seit / since 1998

Hum 201
In tausend Ängsten · Retreat To Safety

Modell-Nr. Model No.	Größe / Size cm / inch	Modellierdatum Sculpting Date	
202	22,5 / 8.75	1948	CE

Hum 202
Opa, Zeitung lesend
Old Man Reading Newspaper
Tischlampe · Table Lamp

Anmerkung/Note:

Vom Kloster Sießen nicht genehmigt. Kein Verkauf, nur Musterfertigung.

Not approved by the Convent of Siessen. Never distributed, archives samples only.

Modell-Nr. Model No.	Größe / Size cm / inch	Modellierdatum Sculpting Date	
203/2/0	10 / 4.00	1953	CE
203/I	14 / 5.50	1948	CE

Anmerkung/Note:

Letzte Ausgabe 1990, Sonderbodenbild und Plombe im letzten Produktionsjahr.

Final Issue 1990, special backstamp and medallion in the last year of production.

Hum 203
Frühlingsidyll · Signs Of Spring

OE: Offene Edition / Open Edition
CE: Produktion beendet / Closed Edition
TWD: Vorübergehend nicht mehr in Produktion / Temporarily withdrawn from production

Modell-Nr. Model No.	Größe / Size cm / inch	Modellierdatum Sculpting Date	
204	14,5 / 5.75	1949	TWD seit / since 98

Hum 204
In Lauterbach hab' i'... · Weary Wanderer

Anmerkung/Note:

Erste Muster wurden mit blauen Augen produziert.

Old samples occasionally with blue eyes.

Modell-Nr. Model No.	Größe / Size cm / inch	Modellierdatum Sculpting Date	
205	11,5 / 4.50	1949	CE

Anmerkung/Note:

Hum 208 Französisch · French

Hum 209 Schwedisch · Swedish

Hum 210 Für "Schmid Bros. Inc. Boston" einem früheren Importeur der M.I.Hummel Figuren in den USA.

For "Schmid Bros. Inc. Boston" a former importer of M.I.Hummel figurines.

Hum 211 Englisch · English

Hum 213 Spanisch · Spanish

Hum 205
Händler Aufstellschild · Dealer's Plaque
Deutsch · German

Modell-Nr. Model No.	Größe / Size cm / inch	Modellierdatum Sculpting Date	
206	12 / 4.75	1949	TWD seit / since 98

Hum 206
Engel auf Wolke · Angel Cloud
Weihkessel · Holy Water Font

OE: Offene Edition / Open Edition
CE: Produktion beendet / Closed Edition
TWD: Vorübergehend nicht mehr in Produktion / Temporarily withdrawn from production

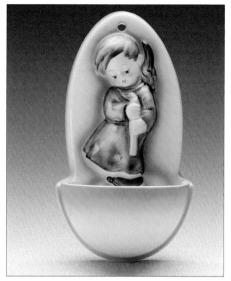

Modell-Nr. Model No.	Größe / Size cm / inch	Modellierdatum Sculpting Date	
207	12 / 4.75	1949	OE

Hum 207
Christkindlein kommt · Heavenly Angel
Weihkessel · Holy Water Font

Hum 208 – 213

siehe Seite 91 (Hum 205)

see page 91 (Hum 205)

OE: Offene Edition / Open Edition
CE: Produktion beendet / Closed Edition
TWD: Vorübergehend nicht mehr in Produktion / Temporarily withdrawn from production

Hum 214/I Krippe · Nativity Set		Modell-Nr. Model No.		Größe / Size cm / inch	Modellierdatum Sculpting Date	
	①	214/A/M/I	Mutter Maria, Virgin Mary	16,5 / 6.50	1951	OE
	②	214/A/K/I	Jesuskind, Infant Jesus	4 / 3.50	1951	OE
	③	214/B/I	Josef, Joseph	19 / 7.50	1951	OE
	④	214/C/I	Angenehme Ruhe, Good Night	9 / 3.50	1951	OE
	⑤	214/D/I	Fromme Weisen, Angel Serenade	8 / 3.25	1951	OE
	⑥	214/E/I	Wir gratulieren, We Congratulate	9 / 3.50	1951	OE
	⑦	214/F/I	Hirte stehend, Shepherd standing	18 / 7.00	1951	OE
	⑧	214/G/I	Hirte kniend, Shepherd kneeling	12 / 4.75	1951	OE
	⑨	214/H/I	Schäferbub, Little Tooter	10 / 4.00	1951	OE
	⑩	214/J/I	Esel, Donkey	13 / 5.25	1951	OE
	⑪	214/K/I	Ochse, Ox	9 / 3.50	1951	OE
	⑫	214/L/I	Mohrenkönig, Moorish King	21 / 8.25	1951	OE
	⑬	214/M/I	König kniend, King kneeling	14 / 5.50	1951	OE
	⑭	214/N/I	König mit Kassette, King with cashbox	14 / 5.50	1951	OE
	⑮	214/O/I	Lämmchen, Lamb	4 / 1.75	1951	OE

OE: Offene Edition / Open Edition
CE: Produktion beendet / Closed Edition
TWD: Vorübergehend nicht mehr in Produktion / Temporarily withdrawn from production

Hum 214/0 Krippe · Nativity Set		Modell-Nr. Model No.		Größe / Size cm / inch	Modellierdatum Sculpting Date	
	①	214/A/M/0	Mutter Maria, Virgin Mary	13,5 / 5.50	1985	OE
	②	214/A/K/0	Jesuskind, Infant Jesus	3 / 1.25	1985	OE
	③	214/B/0	Josef, Joseph	15,5 / 6.250	1985	OE
	④	214/D/0	Fromme Weisen, Angel Serenade	7 / 2.75	1999	OE
	⑤	214/F/0	Hirte stehend, Shepherd standing	14 / 5.50	1991	OE
	⑥	214/G/0	Hirte kniend, Shepherd kneeling	10 / 4.00	1991	OE
	⑦	214/H/0	Schäferbub, Little Tooter	8 / 3.25	1991	OE
	⑧	214/J/0	Esel, Donkey	10 / 4.00	1951	OE
	⑨	214/K/0	Ochse, Ox	7 / 2.75	1951	OE
	⑩	214/L/0	Mohrenkönig, Moorish King	16 / 6.25	1987	OE
	⑪	214/M/0	König kniend, King kneeling	11 / 4.25	1987	OE
	⑫	214/N/0	König mit Kassette,	10,5 / 4.25	1987	OE
			King with cashbox			OE
	⑬	214/O/0	Lämmchen, Lamb	2,5 / 1.00	1987	OE

Anmerkung/Note:

214/F/0, G/0, H/0 Erste Ausgabe 1991 mit Sonderbodenbild im ersten Produktionsjahr.

214/F/0, G/0, H/0 First Issue 1991 with special backstamp in the first year of production.

214/D/0 Erste Ausgabe 1999 mit Sonderbodenbild im ersten Produktionsjahr.

214/D/0 First Issue 1999 with special backstamp in the first year of production.

OE: Offene Edition / Open Edition
CE: Produktion beendet / Closed Edition
TWD: Vorübergehend nicht mehr in Produktion / Temporarily withdrawn from production

Modell-Nr. Model No.	Größe / Size cm / inch	Modellierdatum Sculpting Date	
217	14 / 5.50	1951	OE

Hum 217
Schmerz laß nach · Boy With Toothache

Modell-Nr. Model No.	Größe / Size cm / inch	Modellierdatum Sculpting Date	
218/2/0	11 / 4.25	1953	OE
218/0	13 / 5.25	1952	TWD seit / since 1998

Hum 218
Geburtstagsständchen · Birthday Serenade

Modell-Nr. Model No.	Größe / Size cm / inch	Modellierdatum Sculpting Date	
219	9,5 / 3.75	1952	CE

Hum 219
Mädchen mit Frosch · Little Velma

OE: Offene Edition / Open Edition
CE: Produktion beendet / Closed Edition
TWD: Vorübergehend nicht mehr in Produktion / Temporarily withdrawn from production

Modell-Nr. Model No.	Größe / Size cm / inch	Modellierdatum Sculpting Date	
220	10 / 4.00	1952	OE

Hum 220
Wir gratulieren · We Congratulate

Modell-Nr. Model No.	Größe / Size cm / inch	Modellierdatum Sculpting Date	
221	15 / 6.00	1952	CE

Anmerkung/Note:

Kein Verkauf, nur Musterfertigung.

Never distributed, archives samples only.

Hum 221
Strickliesl · Happy Pastime
Dose · Box

Modell-Nr. Model No.	Größe / Size cm / inch	Modellierdatum Sculpting Date	
222	12,5 / 5.00	1952	CE

Hum 222
Madonnenbild · Madonna
Wandbild · Wall Plaque

OE: Offene Edition / Open Edition
CE: Produktion beendet / Closed Edition
TWD: Vorübergehend nicht mehr in Produktion / Temporarily withdrawn from production

Modell-Nr. Model No.	Größe / Size cm / inch	Modellierdatum Sculpting Date	
223	24,5 / 9.75	1952	TWD

Hum 223
Brüderlein und Schwesterlein · To Market
Tischlampe · Table Lamp

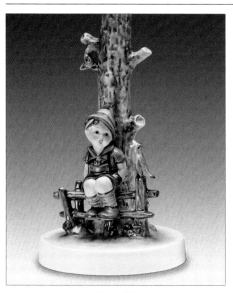

Modell-Nr. Model No.	Größe / Size cm / inch	Modellierdatum Sculpting Date	
224/I	19 / 7.50	1952	OE
224/II	24 / 9.50	1952	TWD

Hum 224
Vaters G'scheitester · Wayside Harmony
Tischlampe · Table Lamp

Modell-Nr. Model No.	Größe / Size cm / inch	Modellierdatum Sculpting Date	
225/I	19 / 7.50	1952	OE
225/II	24 / 9.50	1952	TWD

Hum 225
Mutters Liebste · Just Resting
Tischlampe · Table Lamp

OE: Offene Edition / Open Edition
CE: Produktion beendet / Closed Edition
TWD: Vorübergehend nicht mehr in Produktion / Temporarily withdrawn from production

Modell-Nr. Model No.	Größe / Size cm / inch	Modellierdatum Sculpting Date	
226	11 x 16	1952	OE
	4.25 x 6.25		

Hum 226
Trara-die Post ist da · The Mail Is Here

Modell-Nr. Model No.	Größe / Size cm / inch	Modellierdatum Sculpting Date	
227	19 / 7.50	1953	TWD

Hum 227
Liebt mich, liebt mich nicht...
She Loves Me, She Loves Me Not...
Tischlampe · Table Lamp

Modell-Nr. Model No.	Größe / Size cm / inch	Modellierdatum Sculpting Date	
228	19 / 7.50	1953	TWD

Hum 228
Freunde · Good Friends
Tischlampe · Table Lamp

OE: Offene Edition / Open Edition
CE: Produktion beendet / Closed Edition
TWD: Vorübergehend nicht mehr in Produktion / Temporarily withdrawn from production

Modell-Nr. Model No.	Größe / Size cm / inch	Modellierdatum Sculpting Date	
229	19 / 7.50	1953	TWD

Hum 229
Frühling · Apple Tree Girl
Tischlampe · Table Lamp

Modell-Nr. Model No.	Größe / Size cm / inch	Modellierdatum Sculpting Date	
230	19 / 7.50	1953	TWD

Hum 230
Herbst · Apple Tree Boy
Tischlampe · Table Lamp

Modell-Nr. Model No.	Größe / Size cm / inch	Modellierdatum Sculpting Date	
231	25 / 9.75	1954	TWD
234	19,5 / 7.75	1954	TWD

Hum 231, Hum 234
Geburtstagsständchen · Birthday Serenade
Tischlampe · Table Lamp

OE: Offene Edition / Open Edition
CE: Produktion beendet / Closed Edition
TWD: Vorübergehend nicht mehr in Produktion / Temporarily withdrawn from production

Modell-Nr. Model No.	Größe / Size cm / inch	Modellierdatum Sculpting Date	
239/B	9 / 3.50	1967	OE
239/B/X	8 / 3.25	1967	TWD
239/B/O	9 / 3.50	1997	TWD

239/B

239/B/O

Hum 239/ B
Mädchen mit Puppe · Girl With Doll

Anmerkung/Note:

239/B/X Figur ohne Postament, Figurine Without Base.

239/B/O Hängefigur, Ornament.

Modell-Nr. Model No.	Größe / Size cm / inch	Modellierdatum Sculpting Date	
239/ C	9 / 3.50	1967	OE
239/C/X	8 / 3.25	1997	TWD
239/C/O	9 / 3.50	1997	TWD

239/C

239/C/O

Hum 239/ C
Junge mit Holzpferd · Boy With Horse

Anmerkung/Note:

239/C/X Figur ohne Postament, Figurine Without Base.

239/C/O Hängefigur, Ornament.

Modell-Nr. Model No.	Größe / Size cm / inch	Modellierdatum Sculpting Date	
239/D	9 / 3.50	1997	OE
239/D/X	8 / 3.25	1997	TWD
239/D/O	9 / 3.50	1997	TWD

Anmerkung/Note:

239/D/X Figur ohne Postament, Figurine Without Base.

239/D/O Hängefigur, Ornament.

239/D

239/D/O

Hum 239/ D
Mädchen mit Tannenbaum
Girl With Fir Tree

OE: Offene Edition / Open Edition
CE: Produktion beendet / Closed Edition
TWD: Vorübergehend nicht mehr in Produktion / Temporarily withdrawn from production

Modell-Nr. Model No.	Größe / Size cm / inch	Modellierdatum Sculpting Date	
240	11 / 4.25	1955	OE

Hum 240
Trommler · Little Drummer

Modell-Nr. Model No.	Größe / Size cm / inch	Modellierdatum Sculpting Date	
241	26 x 21		TWD
	10.25 x 8.25		

Hum 241
Engelbrücke · Angel Lights
Kerzenhalter · Candle Holder

Modell-Nr. Model No.	Größe / Size cm / inch	Modellierdatum Sculpting Date	
242	11 / 4.25	1955	CE

Anmerkung/Note:

Kein Verkauf, nur Musterfertigung.

Never distributed, archives samples only.

Hum 242
O, du fröhliche... · Joyous News
Weihkessel · Holy Water Font

OE: Offene Edition / Open Edition
CE: Produktion beendet / Closed Edition
TWD: Vorübergehend nicht mehr in Produktion / Temporarily withdrawn from production

Modell-Nr. Model No.	Größe / Size cm / inch	Modellierdatum Sculpting Date	
243	10 / 4.00	1955	OE

Hum 243
Madonna mit Kind · Madonna And Child
Weihkessel · Holy Water Font

Modell-Nr. Model No.	Größe / Size cm / inch	Modellierdatum Sculpting Date	
246	10 / 4.00	1955	OE

Hum 246
Heilige Familie · Holy Family
Weihkessel · Holy Water Font

Modell-Nr. Model No.	Größe / Size cm / inch	Modellierdatum Sculpting Date	
247	11,5 / 4.50	1956	CE

Anmerkung/Note:

Vom Kloster Sießen nicht genehmigt. Kein Verkauf, nur Musterfertigung.

Not approved by the Convent of Siessen. Never distributed, archives samples only.

Hum 247
Rosenkranz-Königin
Standing Madonna with child

OE: Offene Edition / Open Edition
CE: Produktion beendet / Closed Edition
TWD: Vorübergehend nicht mehr in Produktion / Temporarily withdrawn from production

Modell-Nr. Model No.	Größe / Size cm / inch	Modellierdatum Sculpting Date		
248/0	14 / 5.50	1958	TWD scit / since 1998	
248/I	16 / 6.25	1958	CE	

Hum 248
Schutzengel · Guardian Angel
Weihkessel · Holy Water Font

Modell-Nr. Model No.	Größe / Size cm / inch	Modellierdatum Sculpting Date	
249	21 / 8.25	unbekannt, unknown	CE

Anmerkung/Note:

Kein Verkauf, nur Musterfertigung.

Never distributed, archives samples only.

Hum 249
Madonna mit Kind · Madonna With Child
Wandbild · Wall Plaque

Modell-Nr. Model No.	Größe / Size cm / inch	Modellierdatum Sculpting Date		
250/A	14 / 5.50	1960	TWD	Ziegenbub Little Goat Herder
250/B	14 / 5.50	1960	TWD	Im Hühnerhof Feeding Time

Hum 250/A, B
Buchstützen · Book Ends

OE: Offene Edition / Open Edition
CE: Produktion beendet / Closed Edition
TWD: Vorübergehend nicht mehr in Produktion / Temporarily withdrawn from production

Modell-Nr. Model No.	Größe / Size cm / inch	Modellierdatum Sculpting Date		
251/A	13 / 5.25	1960	TWD	Liebt mich, liebt mich nicht...
				She Loves Me, She Loves Me Not...
251/B	13 / 5.25	1960	TWD	Freunde
				Good Friends

Hum 251/B, A
Buchstützen · Book Ends

Modell-Nr. Model No.	Größe / Size cm / inch	Modellierdatum Sculpting Date		
252/A	13 / 5.25	1962	TWD	Herbst
				Apple Tree Boy
252/B	13 / 5.25	1962	TWD	Frühling
				Apple Tree Girl

Hum 252/B, A
Buchstützen · Book Ends

255/I

Modell-Nr. Model No.	Größe / Size cm / inch	Modellierdatum Sculpting Date	
255/4/0	8 / 3.25	1987	CE seit / since 1998
255/I	17 / 6.75	1962	TWD seit / since 1998

Hum 255
Zwei rechts - zwei links · A Stitch In Time

OE: Offene Edition / Open Edition
CE: Produktion beendet / Closed Edition
TWD: Vorübergehend nicht mehr in Produktion / Temporarily withdrawn from production

Modell-Nr. Model No.	Größe / Size cm / inch	Modellierdatum Sculpting Date	
256	19 / 7.50	1962	TWD seit / since 1998

Hum 256
Ob's gelingt? · Knitting Lesson

257/0

Modell-Nr. Model No.	Größe / Size cm / inch	Modellierdatum Sculpting Date	
257/5/0	7 / 2.75	1991	CE
257/2/0	10 / 4.00	1983	OE
257/0	13 / 5.25	1962	OE

Editionen mit Sonderbodenbild/ Editions with special backstamp:

Modell-Nr. Model No.	Ausgabejahr Year	Ausgabeland Country	
257/5/0	1995	"Pen Pals" USA	CE
257/5/0	1997	Bradford, USA	CE
257/0	1999	"Caribbean Collection" Karibik	CE

Hum 257
Für's Mütterchen · For Mother

Modell-Nr. Model No.	Größe / Size cm / inch	Modellierdatum Sculpting Date	
258	13 / 5.25	1962	OE

Hum 258
Rat mal! · Which Hand?

OE: Offene Edition / Open Edition
CE: Produktion beendet / Closed Edition
TWD: Vorübergehend nicht mehr in Produktion / Temporarily withdrawn from production

Modell-Nr. Model No.	Größe / Size cm / inch	Modellierdatum Sculpting Date	
259	10 / 4.00	1962	CE

Keine Archivmuster vorhanden.

No Samples available in our Archives.

Hum 259
Mädchen mit Bandoneon
Girl With Accordion

Anmerkung/Note:

Kein Verkauf, nur Musterfertigung.

Never distributed, archives samples only.

Hum 260
Krippe · Nativity Set

	Modell-Nr. Model No.		Größe / Size cm / inch		Modellierdatum Sculpting Date
①	260/A	Maria, Mary	25 / 9.75	OE	1968
②	260/B	Josef, Saint Joseph	30 / 11.75	OE	1968
③	260/C	Jesuskind, Infant Jesus	15 / 6.00	OE	1968
④	260/D	Angenehme Ruhe, Good Night	13 / 5.25	OE	1968
⑤	260/E	Fromme Weisen, Angel Serenade	16 / 6.25	OE	1968
⑥	260/F	Wir gratulieren, We Congratulate	13 /5.25	OE	1968
⑦	260/G	Hirte stehend, Shepherd standing	29 / 11.50	OE	1968
⑧	260/H	Schafgruppe, Sheep with lamp	10 /4.00	OE	1968
⑨	260/J	Hirtenjunge kniend, Shepherd Boy	18 / 7.00	OE	1968
⑩	260/K	Schäferbub, Little Tooter	14 / 5.50	OE	1968
⑪	260/L	Esel stehend, Donkey standing	19 / 7.50	OE	1968
⑫	260/M	Ochse liegend, Ox lying	15 / 6.00	OE	1968
⑬	260/N	Mohrenkönig, Moorish King	32 / 12.50	OE	1968
⑭	260/O	König stehend, King standing	31 / 12.25	OE	1968
⑮	260/P	König kniend, King kneeling	22 / 8.75	OE	1968
⑯	260/R	Schaf liegend, Sheep lying	8 / 3.25	OE	1968

Hum 261
Stille Nacht · Angel Duet

Modell-Nr. Model No.	Größe / Size cm / inch	Modellierdatum Sculpting Date	
261	13 / 5.25	1968	OE

Editionen mit Sonderbodenbild/ Editions with special backstamp:

Modell-Nr. Model No.	Ausgabejahr Year	Ausgabeland Country	
261	1997	"Merry Christmas" USA	CE
261	1997	"Frohe Weihnacht" Deutschland , Germany	CE

OE: Offene Edition / Open Edition
CE: Produktion beendet / Closed Edition
TWD: Vorübergehend nicht mehr in Produktion / Temporarily withdrawn from production

Modell-Nr. Model No.	Größe / Size cm / inch	Modellierdatum Sculpting Date	
262	9 x 13 3.50 x 5.25	1968	TWD

Hum 262
Wiegenlied · Heavenly Lullaby
Kerzenhalter · Candle Holder

Modell-Nr. Model No.	Größe / Size cm / inch	Modellierdatum Sculpting Date	
263	14 / 5.50	1968	CE

Anmerkung/Note:

Kein Verkauf, nur Musterfertigung.

Never distributed, archives samples only.

Hum 263
Wanderbub · Merry Wanderer
Wandbild · Wall Plaque

Modell-Nr. Model No.	Größe / Size cm / inch	Modellierdatum Sculpting Date	
264	19 / 7.50	1970	CE

Editionen mit Sonderbodenbild/ Editions with special backstamp:

Modell-Nr. Model No.	Ausgabejahr Year	Ausgabeland Country	
264	1971	"Workers Edition" nur für Angestellte von Goebel	CE

Anmerkung/Note:

Jahresteller 1971.

Annual Plate 1971.

Hum 264
Christkindlein kommt · Heavenly Angel

OE: Offene Edition / Open Edition
CE: Produktion beendet / Closed Edition
TWD: Vorübergehend nicht mehr in Produktion / Temporarily withdrawn from production

Hum 265
Hört Ihr Leute · Hear Ye, Hear Ye

Hum 266
Hinaus in die Ferne · Globe-Trotter

Hum 267
Gänseliesl · Goose Girl

Hum 268
Fahrt in die Weihnacht
Ride Into Christmas

Hum 269
Frühling · Apple Tree Girl

Hum 270
Herbst · Apple Tree Boy

Hum 271
Strickliesl · Happy Pastime

Hum 272
's stimmt net · Singing Lesson

Hum 273
Erster Schulgang · School Girl

Hum 274
Geborgen (Junge) · Umbrella Boy

Hum 275
Geborgen (Mädchen) · Umbrella Girl

Hum 276
Eilbote · Postman

Hum 277
Fleißiges Lieschen · Little Helper

Hum 278
Kükenmütterchen · Chick Girl

Hum 279
Hasenvater · Playmates

Modell-Nr. Model No.	Größe / Size cm / inch	Modellierdatum Sculpting Date		
265	19 / 7.50	1970	CE	Jahresteller 1972. Annual Plate 1972.
266	19 / 7.50	1971	CE	Jahresteller 1973. Annual Plate 1973.
267	19 / 7.50	1972	CE	Jahresteller 1974. Annual Plate 1974.
268	19 / 7.50	1974	CE	Jahresteller 1975. Annual Plate 1975.
269	19 / 7.50	1974	CE	Jahresteller 1976. Annual Plate 1976.
270	19 / 7.50	1972	CE	Jahresteller 1977. Annual Plate 1977.
271	19 / 7.50	1972	CE	Jahresteller 1978. Annual Plate 1978.
272	19 / 7.50	1972	CE	Jahresteller 1979. Annual Plate 1979.
273	19 / 7.50	1972	CE	Jahresteller 1980. Annual Plate 1980.
274	19 / 7.50	1972	CE	Jahresteller 1981. Annual Plate 1981.
275	19 / 7.50	1972	CE	Jahresteller 1982. Annual Plate 1982.
276	19 / 7.50	1972	CE	Jahresteller 1983. Annual Plate 1983.
277	19 / 7.50	1972	CE	Jahresteller 1984. Annual Plate 1984.
278	19 / 7.50	1972	CE	Jahresteller 1985. Annual Plate 1985.
279	19 / 7.50	1972	CE	Jahresteller 1986. Annual Plate 1986.

Hum 280
Unter einem Dach · Stormy Weather

Hum 281
Sommertanz · Spring Dance

Hum 282
Auf Wiedersehen · Auf Wiedersehen

Modell-Nr. Model No.	Größe / Size cm / inch	Modellierdatum Sculpting Date		
280	25 / 9.75	1974	CE	Jubiläumsteller 1975. Anniversary Plate 1975.
281	25 / 9.75	1978	CE	Jubiläumsteller 1980. Anniversary Plate 1980.
282	25 / 9.75	1980	CE	Jubiläumsteller 1985. Anniversary Plate 1985.

Anmerkung/Note:

Hum 282 "50 Jahre 1935-1985 M.I.Hummel Figuren".

Hum 283
Im Hühnerhof · Feeding Time

Hum 284
Ziegenbub · Little Goat Herder

Hum 285
Schweinehirt · Farm Boy

Hum 286	Hum 287	Hum 288
Schäferbub · Shepherd's Boy	Mutters Liebste · Just Resting	Vaters G'scheitester · Wayside Harmony

Hum 289
Puppenbad · Doll Bath

Hum 290
Puppendoktor · Doctor

Hum 291
Bleib nicht so lange fort
Come Back Soon

Modell-Nr. Model No.	Größe / Size cm / inch	Modellierdatum Sculpting Date		
283	19 / 7.50	1983	CE	Jahresteller 1987. Annual Plate 1987.
284	19 / 7.50	1983	CE	Jahresteller 1988. Annual Plate 1988.
285	19 / 7.50	1983	CE	Jahresteller 1989. Annual Plate 1989.
286	19 / 7.50	1983	CE	Jahresteller 1990. Annual Plate 1990.
287	19 / 7.50	1983	CE	Jahresteller 1991. Annual Plate 1991.
288	19 / 7.50	1983	CE	Jahresteller 1992. Annual Plate 1992.
289	19 / 7.50	1990	CE	Jahresteller 1993. Annual Plate 1993.
290	19 / 7.50	1990	CE	Jahresteller 1994. Annual Plate 1994.
291	19 / 7.50	1990	CE	Jahresteller 1995. Annual Plate 1995.

Anmerkung/Note:

Jahresteller 1995, letze Ausgabe.

Annual Plate 1995, Final Issue.

Hum 292
Die Gratulantin · Meditation

Hum 293
Für's Vaterle · For Father

Hum 294
Ein süßer Gruß · Sweet Greetings

Hum 295
Hänsel und Gretel · Surprise

Modell-Nr. Model No.	Größe / Size cm / inch	Modellierdatum Sculpting Date	
292	18 / 7.00	1991	CE seit / since 1998
293	18 / 7.00	1991	CE seit / since 1998
294	18 / 7.00	1991	CE seit / since 1998
295	18 / 7.00	1991	CE seit / since 1998

Anmerkung/Note:

Relieftellerserie "In Freundschaft".

Relief Plate Series "Friends Forever".

Hum 296
Winter · Winter Melody

Hum 297
Frühling · Springtime Serenade

Hum 298
Sommer · Summertime Stroll

Modell-Nr. Model No.	Größe / Size cm / inch	Modellierdatum Sculpting Date	
296	19,5 / 7.75	1994	CE seit / since 1998
297	19,5 / 7.75	1995	CE seit / since 1998
298	19,5 / 7.75	1995	CE seit / since 1998
299	19,5 / 7.75	1995	CE seit / since 1998

Anmerkung/Note:

Jahrestellerserie "Die 4 Jahreszeiten".

Annual Plate Series "Four Seasons".

Hum 299
Herbst · Autumn Glory

Modell-Nr. Model No.	Größe / Size cm / inch	Modellierdatum Sculpting Date	
300	13 / 5.25	1954	OE

Hum 300
Tierfreund · Bird Watcher

Modell-Nr. Model No.	Größe / Size cm / inch	Modellierdatum Sculpting Date	
301	15 / 6.00	1957	OE

Hum 301
Weihnachtsengel · Christmas Angel

OE: Offene Edition / Open Edition
CE: Produktion beendet / Closed Edition
TWD: Vorübergehend nicht mehr in Produktion / Temporarily withdrawn from production

Modell-Nr. Model No.	Größe / Size cm / inch	Modellierdatum Sculpting Date	
304	13,5 / 5.25	1955	OE

Hum 304
Kunstmaler · The Artist

Modell-Nr. Model No.	Größe / Size cm / inch	Modellierdatum Sculpting Date	
305	14 / 5.50	1955	OE

Editionen mit Sonderbodenbild/ Editions with special backstamp:

Modell-Nr. Model No.	Ausgabejahr Year	Ausgabeland Country	
305	1997	QVC, USA	CE

Hum 305
Der Schwerarbeiter · The Builder

Modell-Nr. Model No.	Größe / Size cm / inch	Modellierdatum Sculpting Date	
306	12 / 4.75	1955	OE

Hum 306
Stellvertretung · Little Bookkeeper

OE: Offene Edition / Open Edition
CE: Produktion beendet / Closed Edition
TWD: Vorübergehend nicht mehr in Produktion / Temporarily withdrawn from production

Modell-Nr. Model No.	Größe / Size cm / inch	Modellierdatum Sculpting Date	
307	13 / 5.25	1955	OE

Hum 307
Weidmannsheil! · Good Hunting

Modell-Nr. Model No.	Größe / Size cm / inch	Modellierdatum Sculpting Date	
308	14 / 5.50	1955	OE

Hum 308
Schneiderlein · Little Tailor

Modell-Nr. Model No.	Größe / Size cm / inch	Modellierdatum Sculpting Date	
309	9 / 3.50	1955	TWD seit / since 1998

Hum 309
Ein dicker Gruß · With Loving Greetings

OE: Offene Edition / Open Edition
CE: Produktion beendet / Closed Edition
TWD: Vorübergehend nicht mehr in Produktion / Temporarily withdrawn from production

Modell-Nr. Model No.	Größe / Size cm / inch	Modellierdatum Sculpting Date	
310	10 / 4.00	1955	TWD seit / since 1998

Hum 310
Was ist denn da drunten los?
Searching Angel
Wandbild · Wall Plaque

Modell-Nr. Model No.	Größe / Size cm / inch	Modellierdatum Sculpting Date	
311	15 / 6.00	1955	OE

Hum 311
Hab mich lieb! · Kiss Me!

Modell-Nr. Model No.	Größe / Size cm / inch	Modellierdatum Sculpting Date	
312/I	10 / 4.00	1955	OE

Anmerkung/Note:

Treuefigur für Mitglieder des M.I.Hummel Club, die in ihrem fünfzehnten, persönlichen Mitgliedsjahr sind.

Loyalty figurine for members of the M.I.Hummel Club in their 15th personal membership year.

Hum 312
Honiglecker · Honey Lover

OE: Offene Edition / Open Edition
CE: Produktion beendet / Closed Edition
TWD: Vorübergehend nicht mehr in Produktion / Temporarily withdrawn from production

Hum 314
Zwiegespräch · Confidentially

Modell-Nr. Model No.	Größe / Size cm / inch	Modellierdatum Sculpting Date	
314	15 / 6.00	1955	TWD seit / since 1998

Hum 315
I' hab's erreicht · Mountaineer

Modell-Nr. Model No.	Größe / Size cm / inch	Modellierdatum Sculpting Date	
315	13 / 5.25	1955	OE

Editionen mit Sonderbodenbild/ Editions with special backstamp:

Modell-Nr. Model No.	Ausgabejahr Year	Ausgabeland Country	
315	1997	"M.I.Hummel Club Convention" USA	CE
315	2000	Österreich, Austria	CE

Hum 317
Nix für dich! · Not For You

Modell-Nr. Model No.	Größe / Size cm / inch	Modellierdatum Sculpting Date	
317	14 / 5.50	1955	OE

OE: Offene Edition / Open Edition
CE: Produktion beendet / Closed Edition
TWD: Vorübergehend nicht mehr in Produktion / Temporarily withdrawn from production

Hum 318
Der Kunstkritiker · Art Critic

Modell-Nr. Model No.	Größe / Size cm / inch	Modellierdatum Sculpting Date	
318	14 / 5.50	1955	TWD seit / since 1998

Anmerkung/Note:

Erste Ausgabe 1991 mit Sonderbodenbild im ersten Produktionsjahr.

First Issue 1991 with special backstamp in the first year of production.

Hum 319
Puppenbad · Doll Bath

Modell-Nr. Model No.	Größe / Size cm / inch	Modellierdatum Sculpting Date	
319	13 / 5.25	1956	OE

Hum 320
Der Professor · The Professor

Modell-Nr. Model No.	Größe / Size cm / inch	Modellierdatum Sculpting Date	
320/0	12 / 4.75	1989	OE

Anmerkung/Note:

Erste Ausgabe 1992 mit Sonderbodenbild im ersten Produktionsjahr.

First Issue 1992 with special backstamp in the first year of production.

OE: Offene Edition / Open Edition
CE: Produktion beendet / Closed Edition
TWD: Vorübergehend nicht mehr in Produktion / Temporarily withdrawn from production

Modell-Nr. Model No.	Größe / Size cm / inch	Modellierdatum Sculpting Date	
321/4/0	8 / 3.25	1986	CE seit / since 1998
321/I	14,5 / 5.75	1955	OE

321/4/0

321/I

Hum 321
Große Wäsche · Wash Day

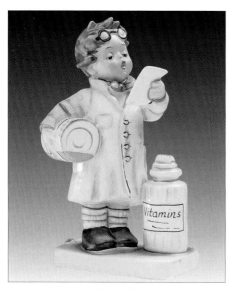

Modell-Nr. Model No.	Größe / Size cm / inch	Modellierdatum Sculpting Date	
322	14 / 5.50	1955	OE

Anmerkung/Note:

Etikett auf Flasche in verschiedenen Versionen.

Several variatious on label of bottle possible.

Hum 322
Der Apotheker · Little Pharmacist

Modell-Nr. Model No.	Größe / Size cm / inch	Modellierdatum Sculpting Date	
323	13 / 5.25	1955	TWD seit / since 1998

Hum 323
Frohe Weihnachten · Merry Christmas
Wandbild · Wall Plaque

OE: Offene Edition / Open Edition
CE: Produktion beendet / Closed Edition
TWD: Vorübergehend nicht mehr in Produktion / Temporarily withdrawn from production

Modell-Nr. Model No.	Größe / Size cm / inch	Modellierdatum Sculpting Date	
327	13,5 / 5.50	1955	OE

Editionen mit Sonderbodenbild/ Editions with special backstamp:

Modell-Nr. Model No.	Ausgabejahr Year	Ausgabeland Country	
327	1998	QVC, USA	CE

Hum 327
Der frohe Wanderer · The Run-A-Way

Modell-Nr. Model No.	Größe / Size cm / inch	Modellierdatum Sculpting Date	
328	15 / 6.00	1955	CE

Editionen mit Sonderbodenbild/ Editions with special backstamp:

Modell-Nr. Model No.	Ausgabejahr Year	Ausgabeland Country	
328	2000	"Retirement Exclusive" USA	CE

Anmerkung/Note:

Letzte Ausgabe 2000, Sonderbodenbild und Plombe im letzten Produktionsjahr.

Final Issue 2000, special backstamp and medallion in the last year of production.

Hum 328
Fastnacht · Carnival

Modell-Nr. Model No.	Größe / Size cm / inch	Modellierdatum Sculpting Date	
330	13 / 5.25	1955	TWD seit / since 1998

Hum 330
Die Bäckerin · Baking Day

OE: Offene Edition / Open Edition
CE: Produktion beendet / Closed Edition
TWD: Vorübergehend nicht mehr in Produktion / Temporarily withdrawn from production

Modell-Nr. Model No.	Größe / Size cm / inch	Modellierdatum Sculpting Date	
331	17 / 6.75	1955	OE

Hum 331
Am Scheideweg · Crossroads

Hum 331
Am Scheideweg · Crossroads
Sonderausgabe · Special Edition

Sonderausgabe "Am Scheideweg" 1990

Auf 20.000 Stück weltweit limitiert und einzeln nummeriert.

Produktion beendet.

Special Commemorative Edition "Crossroads" 1990

Worldwide limited and numbered edition of 20,000 pcs.

Closed Edition.

Hum 331
Am Scheideweg · Crossroads
Sonderausgabe · Special Edition

Sonderausgabe "Berliner Mauer" nur für US-Truppen 1992

Zum Gedenken an die Verdienste des US-Militärs bei der Wahrung der Freiheit West-Berlins.

Auf 20.000 Stück weltweit limitiert und einzeln nummeriert.

Produktion beendet.

20 x 23 x 16,5 cm

Commemorative Edition "Crossroads Freedom Edition" for U.S. Military 1992

recognizes the distinguished achievements of the U.S. military forces in preserving peace and freedom.

Worldwide limited and numbered edition of 20,000 pcs.

Closed Edition.

8.00 x 9.00 x 6.50 inch

Modell-Nr. Model No.	Größe / Size cm / inch	Modellierdatum Sculpting Date	
332	15 / 6.00	1955	TWD seit / since 1998

Hum 332
Stillgestanden! · Soldier Boy

Hum 332
Stillgestanden! · Soldier Boy
Sonderausgabe · Special Edition

Sonderausgabe "Checkpoint Charlie" nur für US-Truppen 1994

- ein Symbol des geteilten Berlin und zugleich der Freiheit West-Berlins, die durch die

Anwesenheit US-amerikanischer Truppen garantiert wurde.

Auf 20.000 Stück weltweit limitiert und einzeln nummeriert.

Produktion beendet.

24 x 23 x 16,5 cm

Commemorative Edition "Checkpoint Charlie" for U.S. Military 1994

one of the symbols of the Cold War and a symbol that confirmed the guarantee of the USA

for the freedom of West-Berlin.

Worldwide limited and numbered edition of 20,000 pcs.

Closed Edition.

9.50 x 9.00 x 6.50 inch

Hum 333
Das große Ereignis · Blessed Event

Modell-Nr. Model No.	Größe / Size cm / inch	Modellierdatum Sculpting Date	
333	13,5 / 5.50	1955	OE

OE: Offene Edition / Open Edition
CE: Produktion beendet / Closed Edition
TWD: Vorübergehend nicht mehr in Produktion / Temporarily withdrawn from production

Modell-Nr. Model No.	Größe / Size cm / inch	Modellierdatum Sculpting Date	
334	13 / 5.25	1956	TWD seit / since 1998

Hum 334
Heimkehr vom Felde · Homeward Bound

Modell-Nr. Model No.	Größe / Size cm / inch	Modellierdatum Sculpting Date	
335/0	11,5 / 4.50	1989	CE
335/I		1956	-------------

Sonderausgabe 1995 / 96

Auf 25.000 Stück weltweit limitiert und einzeln nummeriert.
Davon 15.000 Stück mit "60 Jahre M.I.Hummel Figuren" und 10.000 Stück mit
"125 Jahre Goebel" Sonderbodenbild.
Produktion beendet.

Limited Edition 1995 / 96

Worldwide limited and numbered edition of 25,000 pcs.
15,000 pcs with "60th M.I.Hummel Anniversary" and 10,000 pcs with "125th
Goebel Anniversary" special backstamp.
Closed Edition.

Anmerkung/Note:

335/I Noch nicht veröffentlicht.

335/I Possible Future Edition.

Hum 335
Glücksbub · Lucky Boy

Modell-Nr. Model No.	Größe / Size cm / inch	Modellierdatum Sculpting Date	
336	13,5 / 5.50	1956	OE

Hum 336
Geburtstagsständchen · Close Harmony

OE: Offene Edition / Open Edition
CE: Produktion beendet / Closed Edition
TWD: Vorübergehend nicht mehr in Produktion / Temporarily withdrawn from production

126

Modell-Nr. Model No.	Größe / Size cm / inch	Modellierdatum Sculpting Date	
337	11,5 / 4.50	1956	OE

Hum 337
Aschenputtel · Cinderella

Modell-Nr. Model No.	Größe / Size cm / inch	Modellierdatum Sculpting Date	
338	9 / 3.50	1956	TWD seit / since 1998

Hum 338
Der Geburtstagskuchen · Birthday Cake
Kerzenhalter · Candle Holder

Hum 339
Wir gehen spazieren · Behave!

Modell-Nr. Model No.	Größe / Size cm / inch	Modellierdatum Sculpting Date	
339	14 / 5.50	1956	OE

Anmerkung/Note:

Treuefigur für Mitglieder des M.I.Hummel Club, die in ihrem zwanzigsten,

persönlichen Mitgliedsjahr sind.

Loyalty figurine for members of the M.I.Hummel Club in their 20th personal

membership year.

OE: Offene Edition / Open Edition
CE: Produktion beendet / Closed Edition
TWD: Vorübergehend nicht mehr in Produktion / Temporarily withdrawn from production

Modell-Nr. Model No.	Größe / Size cm / inch	Modellierdatum Sculpting Date	
340	18 / 7.00	1956	OE

Hum 340
Brief ans Christkind
Letter To Santa Claus

Modell-Nr. Model No.	Größe / Size cm / inch	Modellierdatum Sculpting Date	
341/3/0	10 / 4.00	1989	OE
341/I	13,5 / 5.25	1956	-------------

Editionen mit Sonderbodenbild/ Editions with special backstamp:

Modell-Nr. Model No.	Ausgabejahr Year	Ausgabeort Country	
341/3/0	1994	"Special Event" USA	CE

Anmerkung/Note:

341/3/0 Erste Ausgabe 1994 mit Sonderbodenbild im ersten Produktionsjahr,

First Issue 1994 with special backstamp in the first year of production.

341/I Noch nicht veröffentlicht, Possible future Edition.

Hum 341
Das Geburtstagsgeschenk
Birthday Present

Modell-Nr. Model No.	Größe / Size cm / inch	Modellierdatum Sculpting Date	
342	12,5 / 5.00	1956	TWD seit / since 1995

Hum 342
Der Störenfried · Mischief Maker

OE: Offene Edition / Open Edition
CE: Produktion beendet / Closed Edition
TWD: Vorübergehend nicht mehr in Produktion / Temporarily withdrawn from production

Modell-Nr. Model No.	Größe / Size cm / inch	Modellierdatum Sculpting Date	
343/4/0	9 / 3.50	1990	OE
343/I	16,5 / 6.50	1956	OE

343/I

Hum 343
Weihnachtslied · Christmas Song

Anmerkung/Note:

343/4/0 Erste Ausgabe 1996 mit Sonderbodenbild im ersten Produktionsjahr.

First Issue 1996 with special backstamp in the first year of production.

343/4/0

Modell-Nr. Model No.	Größe / Size cm / inch	Modellierdatum Sculpting Date	
344	11 / 4.25	1956	OE

Hum 344
Schwanenteich · Feathered Friends

Modell-Nr. Model No.	Größe / Size cm / inch	Modellierdatum Sculpting Date	
345	15 / 6.00	1956	TWD seit / since 1998

Hum 345
Der Kaufmann · A Fair Measure

OE: Offene Edition / Open Edition
CE: Produktion beendet / Closed Edition
TWD: Vorübergehend nicht mehr in Produktion / Temporarily withdrawn from production

Modell-Nr. Model No.	Größe / Size cm / inch	Modellierdatum Sculpting Date	
346	11,5 / 4.50	1956	OE

Hum 346
Das kluge Schwesterlein
The Smart Little Sister

Modell-Nr. Model No.	Größe / Size cm / inch	Modellierdatum Sculpting Date	
347	19 x 20,5	1957	OE
	7.50 x 8.25		

Hum 347
Die Sieben Schwaben
Adventure Bound, The Seven Swabians

Modell-Nr. Model No.	Größe / Size cm / inch	Modellierdatum Sculpting Date	
348	18 / 7.00	1957	OE

Hum 348
Ringelreihen · Ring Around The Rosie

OE: Offene Edition / Open Edition
CE: Produktion beendet / Closed Edition
TWD: Vorübergehend nicht mehr in Produktion / Temporarily withdrawn from production

Modell-Nr. Model No.	Größe / Size cm / inch	Modellierdatum Sculpting Date	
350	10,5 / 4.25	1964	OE

Hum 350
Zum Festtag · On Holiday

Modell-Nr. Model No.	Größe / Size cm / inch	Modellierdatum Sculpting Date	
351	11,5 / 4.50	1965	OE

Hum 351
Enzian-Mädchen · The Botanist

Modell-Nr. Model No.	Größe / Size cm / inch	Modellierdatum Sculpting Date	
352	10,5 / 4.25	1964	OE

Hum 352
Ein süßer Gruß · Sweet Greetings

OE: Offene Edition / Open Edition
CE: Produktion beendet / Closed Edition
TWD: Vorübergehend nicht mehr in Produktion / Temporarily withdrawn from production

Modell-Nr. Model No.	Größe / Size cm / inch	Modellierdatum Sculpting Date	
353/0	13,5 / 5.50	1962	OE
353/I	17 / 6.75	1962	TWD

Hum 353
Sommertanz · Spring Dance

Editionen mit Sonderbodenbild/ Editions with special backstamp:

Modell-Nr. Model No.	Ausgabejahr Year	Ausgabeort Country	
353/0	1999	"Caribbean Collection" Karibik	CE

Hum 354/A
Kniender Engel mit Laterne
Guiding Angel
Weihkessel · Holy Water Font

Hum 354/B
Engel mit Horn · Tuneful Angel

Weihkessel · Holy Water Font

Hum 354/C
Engel mit Vogel · Angel With Bird

Weihkessel · Holy Water Font

Modell-Nr. Model No.	Größe / Size cm / inch	Modellierdatum Sculpting Date	
354/A	12,5 / 5.00	1958	CE
354/B	12 / 4.75	1958	CE
354/C	11,5 / 4.50	1958	CE

Anmerkung/Note:

Vom Kloster Sießen nicht genehmigt. Kein Verkauf, nur Musterfertigung.

Not approved by the Convent of Siessen. Never distributed, archives samples only.

OE: Offene Edition / Open Edition
CE: Produktion beendet / Closed Edition
TWD: Vorübergehend nicht mehr in Produktion / Temporarily withdrawn from production

Modell-Nr. Model No.	Größe / Size cm / inch	Modellierdatum Sculpting Date	
355	12 / 4.75	1963	OE

Hum 355
Herbstsegen · Autumn Harvest

Modell-Nr. Model No.	Größe / Size cm / inch	Modellierdatum Sculpting Date	
356	12 / 4.75	1963	OE

Hum 356
Frohes Wandern · Gay Adventure

Modell-Nr. Model No.	Größe / Size cm / inch	Modellierdatum Sculpting Date	
357	7 / 2.75	1958	OE

Hum 357
Kniender Engel mit Laterne
Guiding Angel

OE: Offene Edition / Open Edition
CE: Produktion beendet / Closed Edition
TWD: Vorübergehend nicht mehr in Produktion / Temporarily withdrawn from production

Modell-Nr. Model No.	Größe / Size cm / inch	Modellierdatum Sculpting Date	
365	7 / 2.75	1963	CE

Hum 365
Hummele · Hummele

Anmerkung/Note:

Exklusive Sonderedition für M.I.Hummel Clubmitglieder für das Clubjahr 1999/2000.

Exclusive special Edition for members of the M.I.Hummel Club in Club Year 1999/2000.

366/I

Modell-Nr. Model No.	Größe / Size cm / inch	Modellierdatum Sculpting Date	
366/0	8 / 3.25	1987	OE
366/I	9 / 3.50	1987	OE

Hum 366
Hängeengel · Flying Angel

Modell-Nr. Model No.	Größe / Size cm / inch	Modellierdatum Sculpting Date	
367	11 / 4.25	1962	OE

Hum 367
Musterschülerin · Busy Student

OE: Offene Edition / Open Edition
CE: Produktion beendet / Closed Edition
TWD: Vorübergehend nicht mehr in Produktion / Temporarily withdrawn from production

Modell-Nr. Model No.	Größe / Size cm / inch	Modellierdatum Sculpting Date	
369	18 / 7.00	1964	OE

Hum 369
Mach mit! · Follow The Leader

Modell-Nr. Model No.	Größe / Size cm / inch	Modellierdatum Sculpting Date	
371	12 / 4.75	1964	OE

Hum 371
Vatertag · Daddy's Girls

Modell-Nr. Model No.	Größe / Size cm / inch	Modellierdatum Sculpting Date	
373	11 / 4.25	1964	TWD seit / since 1998

Editionen mit Sonderbodenbild/ Editions with special backstamp:

Modell-Nr. Model No.	Ausgabejahr Year	Ausgabeland Country	
373	1999	"M.I.Hummel Club Convention",USA	CE

Hum 373
Der Fischer · Just Fishing

OE: Offene Edition / Open Edition
CE: Produktion beendet / Closed Edition
TWD: Vorübergehend nicht mehr in Produktion / Temporarily withdrawn from production

Modell-Nr. Model No.	Größe / Size cm / inch	Modellierdatum Sculpting Date	
374	11,5 / 4.50	1965	OE

Hum 374
Hab' mein Strumpf verloren
Lost Stocking

Modell-Nr. Model No.	Größe / Size cm / inch	Modellierdatum Sculpting Date	
375/3/0	9 / 3.50	1990	OE
375/0	12 / 4.75	1964	-------------

Anmerkung/Note:

375/3/0 Erste Ausgabe 1994 mit Sonderbodenbild im ersten Produktionsjahr.

First Issue 1994 with special backstamp in the first year of production.

375/0 Noch nicht veröffentlicht, Possible Future Edition.

Hum 375
Ausfahrt · Morning Stroll

Modell-Nr. Model No.	Größe / Size cm / inch	Modellierdatum Sculpting Date	
376	10,5 / 4.25	1965	OE

Editionen mit Sonderbodenbild/ Editions with special backstamp:

Modell-Nr. Model No.	Ausgabejahr Year	Ausgabeland Country	
376	1999	"Caribbean Collection", Karibik	CE

Hum 376
Hänsel, merk dir das · Little Nurse

OE: Offene Edition / Open Edition
CE: Produktion beendet / Closed Edition
TWD: Vorübergehend nicht mehr in Produktion / Temporarily withdrawn from production

Modell-Nr. Model No.	Größe / Size cm / inch	Modellierdatum Sculpting Date	
377/3/0	9,5 / 3.75	1998	-------------
377/0	12 / 4.75	1966	OE

Hum 377
Vergißmeinnicht · Bashful

Anmerkung/Note:

377/3/0 Noch nicht veröffentlicht, Possible Future Edition.

Modell-Nr. Model No.	Größe / Size cm / inch	Modellierdatum Sculpting Date	
378	13 / 5.25	1966	OE

Hum 378
Ostergruß · Easter Greetings

Modell-Nr. Model No.	Größe / Size cm / inch	Modellierdatum Sculpting Date	
380	12,5 / 5.00	1966	CE

Anmerkung/Note:

Exklusive Jahresedition für M.I.Hummel Clubmitglieder für das Clubjahr 1981/1982.

Exclusive Annual Edition for members of the M.I.Hummel Club in Club Year 1981/1982.

Hum 380
Er liebt mich · Daisies Don't Tell

OE: Offene Edition / Open Edition
CE: Produktion beendet / Closed Edition
TWD: Vorübergehend nicht mehr in Produktion / Temporarily withdrawn from production

Modell-Nr. Model No.	Größe / Size cm / inch	Modellierdatum Sculpting Date	
381	13 / 5.25	1966	OE

Hum 381
Zum Blumenmarkt · Flower Vendor

Modell-Nr. Model No.	Größe / Size cm / inch	Modellierdatum Sculpting Date	
382	12,5 / 5.00	1966	OE

Hum 382
Krankenbesuch · Visiting An Invalid

Modell-Nr. Model No.	Größe / Size cm / inch	Modellierdatum Sculpting Date	
383	12 / 4.75	1966	OE

Hum 383
Wanderfreunde · Going Home

OE: Offene Edition / Open Edition
CE: Produktion beendet / Closed Edition
TWD: Vorübergehend nicht mehr in Produktion / Temporarily withdrawn from production

Modell-Nr. Model No.	Größe / Size cm / inch	Modellierdatum Sculpting Date	
384	10,5 / 4.25	1967	OE

Hum 384
Osterfreunde · Easter Time

Modell-Nr. Model No.	Größe / Size cm / inch	Modellierdatum Sculpting Date	
385/4/0	8 / 3.25	1986	CE seit / since 1998
385/3/0	10 / 4.00	1989	-------------
385/I	12 / 4.75	1967	OE

385/I

Hum 385
Kükenliesl · Chicken-Licken

Anmerkung/Note:

385/4/0 Erste Ausgabe 1991 mit
Sonderbodenbild im ersten Produktionsjahr.

First Issue 1991 with special backstamp in the
first year of production.

385/3/0 Noch nicht veröffentlicht, Possible
Future Edition.

385/4/0

Modell-Nr. Model No.	Größe / Size cm / inch	Modellierdatum Sculpting Date	
386	13,5 / 5.50	1967	OE

Hum 386
Auf heimlichen Wegen · On Secret Path

OE: Offene Edition / Open Edition
CE: Produktion beendet / Closed Edition
TWD: Vorübergehend nicht mehr in Produktion / Temporarily withdrawn from production

Modell-Nr. Model No.	Größe / Size cm / inch	Modellierdatum Sculpting Date	
387	14 / 5.50	1967	CE

Hum 387
I' hab' Di' gern · Valentine Gift

Anmerkung/Note:

Exklusive Jahresedition für M.I.Hummel Clubmitglieder für das Clubjahr 1977/1978.

Exclusive Annual Edition for members of the M.I.Hummel Club in Club Year 1977/1978.

Modell-Nr. Model No.	Größe / Size cm / inch	Modellierdatum Sculpting Date	
388	7,5 / 3.00	1967	TWD
388/M	7,5 / 3.00	1967	TWD

Hum 388
Kindergruppe · Little Band
Kerzenhalter · Candle Holder

Anmerkung/Note:

388/M Musikdose, Music Box.

Modell-Nr. Model No.	Größe / Size cm / inch	Modellierdatum Sculpting Date	
389	5,5 / 2.25	1968	OE

Hum 389
Die kleine Sängerin
Girl With Sheet Music

OE: Offene Edition / Open Edition
CE: Produktion beendet / Closed Edition
TWD: Vorübergehend nicht mehr in Produktion / Temporarily withdrawn from production

Modell-Nr. Model No.	Größe / Size cm / inch	Modellierdatum Sculpting Date	
390	5,5 / 2.25	1968	OE

Hum 390
Der kleine Akkordeonspieler
Boy With Accordion

Modell-Nr. Model No.	Größe / Size cm / inch	Modellierdatum Sculpting Date	
391	5,5 / 2.25	1968	OE

Hum 391
Die kleine Trompeterin
Girl With Trumpet

Modell-Nr. Model No.	Größe / Size cm / inch	Modellierdatum Sculpting Date	
392	7,5 / 3.00	1968	TWD
392/M	7,5 / 3.00	1968	TWD

Anmerkung/Note:

392/M Musikdose, Music Box.

OE: Offene Edition / Open Edition
CE: Produktion beendet / Closed Edition
TWD: Vorübergehend nicht mehr in Produktion / Temporarily withdrawn from production

Hum 392
Kindergruppe · Group Of Children

Modell-Nr. Model No.	Größe / Size cm / inch	Modellierdatum Sculpting Date	
394	17 / 6.75	1972	OE

Hum 394
Das ängstliche Schwesterlein
Timid Little Sister

Modell-Nr. Model No.	Größe / Size cm / inch	Modellierdatum Sculpting Date	
395/0	11 / 4.25	1989	OE
395/I	16,5 / 6.50	1971	-------------

Anmerkung/Note:

395/0 Erste Ausgabe 1996 mit Sonderbodenbild im ersten Produktionsjahr.

First Issue 1996 with special backstamp in the first year of production.

395/I Noch nicht veröffentlicht, Possible Future Edition.

Hum 395
Hirtenbub · Shepherd Boy

Modell-Nr. Model No.	Größe / Size cm / inch	Modellierdatum Sculpting Date	
396/2/0	11 / 4.25	1981	OE
396/I	14,5 / 5.75	1970	OE
396/III	21,5 / 8.50	1991	-------------

Anmerkung/Note:

396/III Noch nicht veröffentlicht.

396/III Possible Future Edition.

396/2/0

396/I

Hum 396
Fahrt in die Weihnacht
Ride Into Christmas

Editionen mit Sonderbodenbild/
Editions with special backstamp:

Modell-Nr. Model No.	Ausgabejahr Year	Ausgabeland Country	
396/2/0	1997	QVC, USA	CE

Modell-Nr. Model No.	Größe / Size cm / inch	Modellierdatum Sculpting Date	
397/3/0	10 / 4.00	1988	CE
397/I	15 / 6.00	1973	TWD seit / since 1998

397/I

Hum 397
Der Poet · The Poet

Anmerkung/Note:

397/I Erste Ausgabe 1994 mit Sonderbodenbild im ersten Produktionsjahr.

First Issue 1994 with special backstamp in the first year of production.

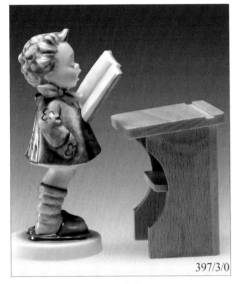

397/3/0

Hum 397
Der Poet · The Poet At The Podium

Anmerkung/Note:

397/3/0 Exklusive Sonderedition für M.I.Hummel Clubmitglieder

für das Clubjahr 1998/1999.

Exclusive Preview Edition for members of the M.I.Hummel Club in

Club Year 1998/1999.

Modell-Nr. Model No.	Größe / Size cm / inch	Modellierdatum Sculpting Date	
399	14,5 / 5.75	1973	CE

Hum 399
Herzjunge · Valentine Joy

Anmerkung/Note:

Exklusive Jahresedition für M.I.Hummel Clubmitglieder für das Clubjahr 1980/1981.

Exclusive Annual Edition for members of the M.I.Hummel Club in Club Year 1980/1981.

OE: Offene Edition / Open Edition
CE: Produktion beendet / Closed Edition
TWD: Vorübergehend nicht mehr in Produktion / Temporarily withdrawn from production

Modell-Nr. Model No.	Größe / Size cm / inch	Modellierdatum Sculpting Date	
403/5/0	7,5 / 3.00	1993	------------
403/I	16 / 6.25	1973	OE

Hum 403
Stiller Genießer · An Apple A Day

Anmerkung/Note:

403/5/0 Noch nicht veröffentlicht, Possible Future Edition.

Modell-Nr. Model No.	Größe / Size cm / inch	Modellierdatum Sculpting Date	
405	12 / 4.75	1973	TWD seit / since 1998

Hum 405
Gefallen's Dir? · Sing With Me

Modell-Nr. Model No.	Größe / Size cm / inch	Modellierdatum Sculpting Date	
406	15,5 / 6.00	1974	CE

Anmerkung/Note:

Zweite Figur der "Century Collection" im Jahre 1987, deren Produktion auf ein Jahr im 20. Jahrhundert beschränkt war. Ein spezieller Sonderbodenstempel und ein Zertifikat bestätigten die Zugehörigkeit zur Serie.

Second figurine in the "Century Collection" in 1987, which was produced for this one year only in the twentieth century. This was attested by a certifitate of authenticity and a special backstamp on the bottom of the figurine.

Hum 406
Frohe Fahrt · Pleasant Journey

Modell-Nr. Model No.	Größe / Size cm / inch	Modellierdatum Sculpting Date	
408/0	12 / 4.75	1983	CE
408/I	15,5 / 6.25	1976	-------------

Hum 408
Gut beschirmt · Smiling Through

Anmerkung/Note:

408/I Noch nicht veröffentlicht, Possible future Edition.

408/0 Exklusive Jahresedition für M.I.Hummel Clubmitglieder

für das Clubjahr 1985/1986.

Exclusive Annual Edition for members of the M.I.Hummel Club

in Club Year 1985/1986.

Modell-Nr. Model No.	Größe / Size cm / inch	Modellierdatum Sculpting Date	
409	10 / 4.00	1976	CE

Hum 409
Brotzeit · Coffee Break

Anmerkung/Note:

Exklusive Jahresedition für M.I.Hummel Clubmitglieder für das Clubjahr 1984/1985.

Exclusive Annual Edition for members of the M.I.Hummel Club

in Club Year 1984/1985.

Modell-Nr. Model No.	Größe / Size cm / inch	Modellierdatum Sculpting Date	
410/3/0	10 / 4.00	1988	-------------
410/I	15 / 6.00	1978	OE

Hum 410
Schulausreißer · Little Architect

Anmerkung/Note:

410/3/0 Noch nicht veröffentlicht, Possible Future Edition.

410/I Erste Ausgabe 1993 mit Sonderbodenbild im ersten Produktionsjahr.

First Issue 1993 with special backstamp in the first year of production.

OE: Offene Edition / Open Edition
CE: Produktion beendet / Closed Edition
TWD: Vorübergehend nicht mehr in Produktion / Temporarily withdrawn from production

Hum 412
Dreckspatz, wasch dich! · Bath Time

Modell-Nr. Model No.	Größe / Size cm / inch	Modellierdatum Sculpting Date	
412	15,5 / 6.25	1977	OE

Hum 413
Ein frohes Lied · Whistler's Duet

Modell-Nr. Model No.	Größe / Size cm / inch	Modellierdatum Sculpting Date	
413	11 / 4.25	1978	TWD seit / since 1998

Anmerkung/Note:

Erste Ausgabe 1992 mit Sonderbodenbild im ersten Produktionsjahr.

First Issue 1992 with special backstamp in the first year of production.

Hum 414
Mach's nach! · In Tune

Modell-Nr. Model No.	Größe / Size cm / inch	Modellierdatum Sculpting Date	
414	9,5 / 3.75	1978	TWD seit / since 1998

OE: Offene Edition / Open Edition
CE: Produktion beendet / Closed Edition
TWD: Vorübergehend nicht mehr in Produktion / Temporarily withdrawn from production

Hum 415
Der Gelehrte · Thoughtful

Modell-Nr. Model No.	Größe / Size cm / inch	Modellierdatum Sculpting Date	
415	11 / 4.25	1979	OE

Editionen mit Sonderbodenbild/ Editions with special backstamp:

Modell-Nr. Model No.	Ausgabejahr Year	Ausgabeland Country	
415	1996	"Grand Cayman" USA	CE
415	1996	"Hummelkrant" Holland,	CE
415	1996	"Hummels And Me..." USA	CE

Hum 416
Zum Jubiläum · Jubilee

Modell-Nr. Model No.	Größe / Size cm / inch	Modellierdatum Sculpting Date	
416	16 / 6.25	1979	CE

Sonderausgabe 1985 · 50 Jahre

Jubiläumsausgabe anläßlich der Markteinführung der M.I. Hummel Figuren im Jahre 1935.

Produktion beendet.

Commemorative Edition 1985 · 50 Years

In celebration of the Golden Anniversary of the introduction of the first M.I.Hummel figurine in 1935.

Closed Edition.

Hum 418
Was gibt's Neues? · What's New?

Modell-Nr. Model No.	Größe / Size cm / inch	Modellierdatum Sculpting Date	
418	13 / 5.25	1980	OE

OE: Offene Edition / Open Edition
CE: Produktion beendet / Closed Edition
TWD: Vorübergehend nicht mehr in Produktion / Temporarily withdrawn from production

Editionen mit Sonderbodenbild/ Editions with special backstamp:

Modell-Nr. Model No.	Ausgabejahr Year	Ausgabeort Country	
418	1995	"St. Peter's Church" Karibik, Caribbean	CE
418	1996	"Insights" Holland, Netherlands	CE
418	1997	"Milwaukee Journal Sentinel" USA	CE
418	1997	"New Braunfels Herald" USA	CE
418	1997	"Grand Cayman BWI" USA	CE
418	1997	"Virgin Islands" USA	CE
418	1998	"Jamaica News" Karibik, Caribbean	CE
418	1998	Karibik	CE
418	1998	"Hadleigh 20th Anniversary" USA	CE
418	1998	USA	CE
418	1999	"Bahamas" Karibik, Caribbean	CE
418	1998	US Militär, US Military	CE

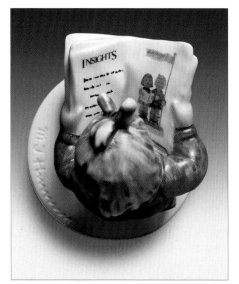

Was gibt's Neues? · What's New?
Club Sonderedition · Club Special Edition

Sonderedition des M.I.Hummel Club

Exklusive Sonderedition mit den jeweiligen Landesflaggen für M.I.Hummel Clubmitglieder für das Clubjahr 1996/1997. Produktion beendet.

Special Edition of the M.I.Hummel Club

Exclusive Special Edition of the particular national flags for members of the M.I.Hummel Club in Club Year 1996/1997. Closed Edition.

Modell-Nr. Model No.	Größe / Size cm / inch	Modellierdatum Sculpting Date	
420	15 / 6.00	1980	OE

Hum 420
Regnet's ? · Is It Raining?

OE: Offene Edition / Open Edition
CE: Produktion beendet / Closed Edition
TWD: Vorübergehend nicht mehr in Produktion / Temporarily withdrawn from production

Hum 421
's ist kalt · It's Cold

Modell-Nr. Model No.	Größe / Size cm / inch	Modellierdatum Sculpting Date	
421	13 / 5.25	1980	CE

Anmerkung/Note:

Exklusive Jahresedition für M.I.Hummel Clubmitglieder für das Clubjahr 1982/1983.

Exclusive Annual Edition for members of the M.I.Hummel Club
in Club Year 1982/1983.

Hum 422
Was jetzt? · What Now?

Modell-Nr. Model No.	Größe / Size cm / inch	Modellierdatum Sculpting Date	
422	14,5 / 5.75	1980	CE

Anmerkung/Note:

Exklusive Jahresedition für M.I.Hummel Clubmitglieder für das Clubjahr 1983/1984.

Exclusive Annual Edition for members of the M.I.Hummel Club
in Club Year 1983/1984.

Hum 423
Der Pferdefreund · Horse Trainer

Modell-Nr. Model No.	Größe / Size cm / inch	Modellierdatum Sculpting Date	
423	11,5 / 4.50	1980	OE

OE: Offene Edition / Open Edition
CE: Produktion beendet / Closed Edition
TWD: Vorübergehend nicht mehr in Produktion / Temporarily withdrawn from production

Modell-Nr. Model No.	Größe / Size cm / inch	Modellierdatum Sculpting Date	
424	12 / 4.75	1980	OE

Hum 424
Schlaf gut · Sleep Tight

Modell-Nr. Model No.	Größe / Size cm / inch	Modellierdatum Sculpting Date	
426/3/0	11 / 4.25	1997	OE
426/II	14,5 / 5.75	1980	-------------

Modell-Nr. Model No.	Ausgabejahr Year	Ausgabeland Country	
426/3/0	2000	„Feldbach" Österreich/Austria	CE

Anmerkung/Note:

426/3/0 Erste Ausgabe 1999 mit Sonderbodenbild im ersten Produktionsjahr.
First Issue 1999 with special backstamp in the first year of production.

426/II Noch nicht veröffentlicht, Possible Future Edition.

Hum 426
Horch! · Pay Attention

Modell-Nr. Model No.	Größe / Size cm / inch	Modellierdatum Sculpting Date	
427/3/0	11 / 4.25	1997	OE
427/II	15 / 6.00	1980	-------------

Anmerkung/Note:

427/3/0 Erste Ausgabe 1999 mit Sonderbodenbild im ersten Produktionsjahr.
First Issue 1999 with special backstamp in the first year of production.

427/II Noch nicht veröffentlicht, Possible Future Edition.

Hum 427
Wo bist Du? · Where Are You?

OE:　　Offene Edition / Open Edition
CE:　　Produktion beendet / Closed Edition
TWD:　Vorübergehend nicht mehr in Produktion / Temporarily withdrawn from production

Modell-Nr. Model No.	Größe / Size cm / inch	Modellierdatum Sculpting Date	
428/3/0	9 / 3.50	1989	OE
428/I	14,5 / 5.75	1980	------------

Anmerkung/Note:

428/3/0 Erste Ausgabe 1998 mit Sonderbodenbild im ersten Produktionsjahr.

First Issue 1998 with special backstamp in the first year of production.

428/I Noch nicht veröffentlicht, Possible Future Edition.

Hum 428
Ich tu' Dir nix · Summertime Surprise

Modell-Nr. Model No.	Größe / Size cm / inch	Modellierdatum Sculpting Date	
429	14 / 5.50	1980	CE

Editionen mit Sonderbodenbild/ Editions with special backstamp:

Modell-Nr. Model No.	Ausgabejahr Year	Ausgabeland Country	
429	1989	"Händlertagung 1989 " Deutschland, Germany	CE

Anmerkung/Note:

Exklusive Jahresedition für M.I.Hummel Clubmitglieder für das Clubjahr 1989/1990.

Exclusive Annual Edition for members of the M.I.Hummel Club

in Club Year 1989/1990.

Hum 429
I bin i · Hello World

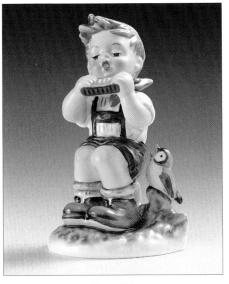

Modell-Nr. Model No.	Größe / Size cm / inch	Modellierdatum Sculpting Date	
430	11 / 4.25	1980	OE

Hum 430
In D-Dur · In D-Major

OE: Offene Edition / Open Edition
CE: Produktion beendet / Closed Edition
TWD: Vorübergehend nicht mehr in Produktion / Temporarily withdrawn from production

Modell-Nr. Model No.	Größe / Size cm / inch	Modellierdatum Sculpting Date	
431	14 / 5.50	1980	CE

Hum 431
Die Überraschung · The Surprise

Anmerkung/Note:

Exklusive Jahresedition für M.I.Hummel Clubmitglieder für das Clubjahr 1988/1989.

Exclusive Annual Edition for members of the M.I.Hummel Club in Club Year 1988/1989.

Modell-Nr. Model No.	Größe / Size cm / inch	Modellierdatum Sculpting Date	
432	7,5 / 3.00	1981	OE

Hum 432
Der erste Strumpf · Knit One, Purl One

Modell-Nr. Model No.	Größe / Size cm / inch	Modellierdatum Sculpting Date	
433	11 / 4.25	1981	TWD seit / since 1998

Hum 433
Auf los geht's los · Sing Along

OE: Offene Edition / Open Edition
CE: Produktion beendet / Closed Edition
TWD: Vorübergehend nicht mehr in Produktion / Temporarily withdrawn from production

Modell-Nr. Model No.	Größe / Size cm / inch	Modellierdatum Sculpting Date	
434	10 / 4.00	1981	OE

Hum 434
Die Heuschrecke · Friend Or Foe?

Anmerkung/Note:

Erste Ausgabe 1991 mit Sonderbodenbild im ersten Produktionsjahr.

First Issue 1991 with special backstamp in the first year of production.

Modell-Nr. Model No.	Größe / Size cm / inch	Modellierdatum Sculpting Date	
435/3/0	10 / 4.00	1988	OE
435/I	15 / 6.00	1981	-------------

Anmerkung/Note:

435/3/0 Erste Ausgabe 1996 mit Sonderbodenbild im ersten Produktionsjahr.

First Issue 1996 with special backstamp in the first year of production.

Hum 435
Schleckerle · Delicious

435/I Noch nicht veröffentlicht, Possible Future Edition.

Modell-Nr. Model No.	Größe / Size cm / inch	Modellierdatum Sculpting Date	
437	15 / 6.00	1982	OE

Hum 437
Der Bombardon · Tuba Player

OE: Offene Edition / Open Edition
CE: Produktion beendet / Closed Edition
TWD: Vorübergehend nicht mehr in Produktion / Temporarily withdrawn from production

Modell-Nr. Model No.	Größe / Size cm / inch	Modellierdatum Sculpting Date	
438	9 / 3.50	1982	OE

Hum 438
Mandolinenklänge · Sounds Of The Mandolin

Modell-Nr. Model No.	Größe / Size cm / inch	Modellierdatum Sculpting Date	
439	13 / 5.25	1982	TWD seit / since 1998

Hum 439
Das Lichtlein brennt · A Gentle Glow
Kerzenhalter · Candle Holder

Modell-Nr. Model No.	Größe / Size cm / inch	Modellierdatum Sculpting Date	
440	13,5 / 5.25	1982	CE

Anmerkung/Note:

Exklusive Jahresedition für M.I.Hummel Clubmitglieder für das Clubjahr 1986/1987.

Exclusive Annual Edition for members of the M.I.Hummel Club in Club Year 1986/1987.

Hum 440
Die Geburtstagstorte · Birthday Candle
Kerzenhalter · Candle Holder

OE: Offene Edition / Open Edition
CE: Produktion beendet / Closed Edition
TWD: Vorübergehend nicht mehr in Produktion / Temporarily withdrawn from production

Modell-Nr. Model No.	Größe / Size cm / inch	Modellierdatum Sculpting Date	
441	33 / 13.00	1982	CE

Anmerkung/Note:

Dritte Figur der "Century Collection" im Jahre 1988, deren Produktion auf ein Jahr im 20. Jahrhundert beschränkt war. Ein spezieller Sonderbodenstempel und ein Zertifikat bestätigten die Zugehörigkeit zur Serie.

Third figurine in the "Century Collection" in 1988, which was produced for this one year only in the twentieth century. This was attested by a certifitate of authenticity and a special backstamp on the bottom of the figurines.

Hum 441
Glockenturm · Call To Worship
Uhr · Clock

Modell-Nr. Model No.	Größe / Size cm / inch	Modellierdatum Sculpting Date	
442	28,5 / 11.25	1982	CE

Anmerkung/Note:

Erste Figur der "Century Collection" im Jahre 1986, deren Produktion auf ein Jahr im 20. Jahrhundert beschränkt war. Ein spezieller Sonderbodenstempel und ein Zertifikat bestätigten die Zugehörigkeit zur Serie.

First figurine in the "Century Collection" in 1986, which was produced for this one year only in the twentieth century. This was attested by a certifitate of authenticity and a special backstamp on the bottom of the figurines.

Hum 442
Bergkirchlein · Chapel Time
Uhr · Clock

Modell-Nr. Model No.	Größe / Size cm / inch	Modellierdatum Sculpting Date	
447	13 / 5.25	1983	CE

Anmerkung/Note:

Exklusive Jahresedition für M.I.Hummel Clubmitglieder für das Clubjahr 1987/1988.
Exclusive Annual Edition for members of the M.I.Hummel Club in Club Year 1987/1988.

Hum 447
Morgenkonzert · Morning Concert

OE: Offene Edition / Open Edition
CE: Produktion beendet / Closed Edition
TWD: Vorübergehend nicht mehr in Produktion / Temporarily withdrawn from production

Modell-Nr. Model No.	Größe / Size cm / inch	Modellierdatum Sculpting Date	
449	13 / 5.25	1984	CE seit Mai 2000
			CE since May 2000

Anmerkung/Note:

Treuefigur für Mirglieder des M.I.Hummel Club, die in ihrem zehnten, persönlichen Mitgliedsjahr sind.

Loyalty figurine for members of the M.I.Hummel Club in their 10th personal membership year.

Hum 449
Brüderlein und Schwesterlein
The Little Pair

Modell-Nr. Model No.	Größe / Size cm / inch	Modellierdatum Sculpting Date	
450/0	13 / 5.25	1989	OE
450/I	14,5 / 5.75	1984	------------

Anmerkung/Note:

450/0 Exklusive Jahresedition für M.I.Hummel Clubmitglieder
für das Clubjahr 2000/2001.

Exclusive Annual Edition for members of the M.I.Hummel Club
in Club Year 2000/2001.

450/I Noch nicht veröffentlicht, Possible Future Edition.

Hum 450
Sticht die? · Will It Sting?

Modell-Nr. Model No.	Größe / Size cm / inch	Modellierdatum Sculpting Date	
451	11 / 4.25	1984	OE

Anmerkung/Note:

Erste Ausgabe 1995 mit Sonderbodenbild im ersten Produktionsjahr.

First Issue 1995 with special backstamp in the first year of production.

Hum 451
Nur ein Viertelstündchen · Just Dozing

OE: Offene Edition / Open Edition
CE: Produktion beendet / Closed Edition
TWD: Vorübergehend nicht mehr in Produktion / Temporarily withdrawn from production

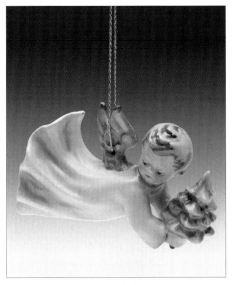

Modell-Nr. Model No.	Größe / Size cm / inch	Modellierdatum Sculpting Date	
452	9 / 3.50	1984	CE

Anmerkung/Note:

Jahres-Christbaumschmuck 1988.

Annual Collectible Ornament 1988.

Hum 452
Christbaumengel · Flying High

Modell-Nr. Model No.	Größe / Size cm / inch	Modellierdatum Sculpting Date	
453	8 / 3.25	1984	OE

Hum 453
Lautenklänge · The Accompanist

Modell-Nr. Model No.	Größe / Size cm / inch	Modellierdatum Sculpting Date	
454	7,5 / 3.00	1984	OE

Hum 454
Lobgesang · Song Of Praise

OE: Offene Edition / Open Edition
CE: Produktion beendet / Closed Edition
TWD: Vorübergehend nicht mehr in Produktion / Temporarily withdrawn from production

Modell-Nr. Model No.	Größe / Size cm / inch	Modellierdatum Sculpting Date	
455	7 / 2.75	1984	OE

Hum 455
Wohl behütet · The Guardian

Anmerkung/Note:

Erste Ausgabe 1991 mit Sonderbodenbild im ersten Produktionsjahr.

First Issue 1991 with special backstamp in the first year of production.

Wohl behütet · The Guardian
Personalisierungsprogramm
Personalisation Program

Anmerkung/Note:

Diese Figur kann mit einer persönlichen Widmung beschriftet werden. Fragen Sie Ihren Fachhändler.

This figurine is available in our Personalisation Program with your own personal message. Just ask your local retailer.

Modell-Nr. Model No.	Größe / Size cm / inch	Modellierdatum Sculpting Date	
457	7,5 / 3.00	1984	OE

Hum 457
Der kleine Trompeter
Sound The Trumpet

OE: Offene Edition / Open Edition
CE: Produktion beendet / Closed Edition
TWD: Vorübergehend nicht mehr in Produktion / Temporarily withdrawn from production

Modell-Nr. Model No.	Größe / Size cm / inch	Modellierdatum Sculpting Date	
458	13 / 5.25	1984	OE

Hum 458
Märchenstunde · Storybook Time

Anmerkung/Note:

Erste Ausgabe 1992 mit Sonderbodenbild im ersten Produktionsjahr.

First Issue 1992 with special backstamp in the first year of production.

Modell-Nr. Model No.	Größe / Size cm / inch	Modellierdatum Sculpting Date	
459	10 / 4.00	1984	OE

Hum 459
Auf der Sommerwiese · In The Meadow

Modell-Nr. Model No.	Größe / Size cm / inch	Modellierdatum Sculpting Date	
460	13 / 5.25	1984	TWD

Hum 460
Händlerschild · Retailer Plaque

Anmerkung/Note:

Das Aufstellschild wurde in neun Sprachversionen für autorisierte Fachhändler produziert, Deutsch, Englisch, Amerikanisch, Holländisch, Italienisch, Französisch, Schwedisch, Spanisch und Japanisch.

This plaque was issued in nine decal variations for authorized dealers for use in other languages, German, British, US, Dutch, Italian, French, Swedish, Spanish and Japanes Version.

OE: Offene Edition / Open Edition
CE: Produktion beendet / Closed Edition
TWD: Vorübergehend nicht mehr in Produktion / Temporarily withdrawn from production

Modell-Nr. Model No.	Größe / Size cm / inch	Modellierdatum Sculpting Date	
463/3/0	10 / 4.00	1990	-------------
463/0	14 / 5.50	1985	CE

Anmerkung/Note:

463/3/0 Noch nicht veröffentlicht. Possible Future Edition.

463/0 Exklusive Jahresedition für M.I.Hummel Clubmitglieder
für das Clubjahr 1992/1993.
Exclusive Annual Edition for members of the M.I.Hummel Club
in Club Year 1992/1993.

Hum 463
Mein Wunsch ist klein · My Wish Is Small

Modell-Nr. Model No.	Größe / Size cm / inch	Modellierdatum Sculpting Date	
467	13 / 5.25	1985	OE

Hum 467
Schulmädchen · The Kindergartner

Modell-Nr. Model No.	Größe / Size cm / inch	Modellierdatum Sculpting Date	
471	25,5 / 10.00	1986	CE

Anmerkung/Note:

Vierte Figur der "Century Collection" im Jahre 1989, deren Produktion auf ein Jahr im
20. Jahrhundert beschränkt war. Ein spezieller Sonderbodenstempel und ein Zertifikat
bestätigten die Zugehörigkeit zur Serie.

Fourth figurine in the "Century Collection" in 1989, which was produced for this one year
only in the twentieth century. This was attested by a certifitate of authenticity and a special
backstamp on the bottom of the figurine.

Hum 471
Sängerquartett · Harmony In Four Parts

OE: Offene Edition / Open Edition
CE: Produktion beendet / Closed Edition
TWD: Vorübergehend nicht mehr in Produktion / Temporarily withdrawn from production

Modell-Nr. Model No.	Größe / Size cm / inch	Modellierdatum Sculpting Date	
472	20 / 8.00	1986	CE

Hum 472
Bald sind wir drüben · On Our Way

Anmerkung/Note:

Siebte Figur der "Century Collection" im Jahre 1992, deren Produktion auf ein Jahr im 20. Jahrhundert beschränkt war. Ein spezieller Sonderbodenstempel und ein Zertifikat bestätigten die Zugehörigkeit zur Serie.

Seventh figurine in the "Century Collection" in 1992, which was produced for this one year only in the twentieth century. This was attested by a certifitate of authenticity and a special backstamp on the bottom of the figurines.

Modell-Nr. Model No.	Größe / Size cm / inch	Modellierdatum Sculpting Date	
473	15,5 / 6.00	1986	CE

Hum 473
Knecht Ruprecht · Ruprecht

Limitierte Ausgabe "Knecht Ruprecht" 1997

Auf 20.000 Stück weltweit limitiert und einzeln nummeriert.
Produktion beendet.

Limited Edition "Ruprecht" 1997

Worldwide limited and numbered edition of 20,000 pcs.
Closed Edition.

Modell-Nr. Model No.	Größe / Size cm / inch	Modellierdatum Sculpting Date	
475	11,5 / 4.50	1986	OE

Hum 475
Die Pusteblume · Make A Wish

OE: Offene Edition / Open Edition
CE: Produktion beendet / Closed Edition
TWD: Vorübergehend nicht mehr in Produktion / Temporarily withdrawn from production

Hum 476
Winterlied · Winter Song

Modell-Nr. Model No.	Größe / Size cm / inch	Modellierdatum Sculpting Date	
476	10 / 4.00	1987	OE

Hum 477
Flötenlied · A Budding Maestro

Modell-Nr. Model No.	Größe / Size cm / inch	Modellierdatum Sculpting Date	
477	10 / 4.00	1987	TWD seit / since 1998

Hum 478
Hallo · I'm Here

Modell-Nr. Model No.	Größe / Size cm / inch	Modellierdatum Sculpting Date	
478	8 / 3.25	1987	OE

OE: Offene Edition / Open Edition
CE: Produktion beendet / Closed Edition
TWD: Vorübergehend nicht mehr in Produktion / Temporarily withdrawn from production

Modell-Nr. Model No.	Größe / Size cm / inch	Modellierdatum Sculpting Date	
479	9 / 3.50	1987	CE

Anmerkung/Note:

Exklusive Begrüßungsfigur für M.I.Hummel Clubmitglieder für die Clubjahre 1989 bis 1996.

Exclusive Welcome Figurine for members of the M.I.Hummel Club in the Club Years 1989 to 1996.

Hum 479
Ich bring Dir was · I Brought You A Gift

Modell-Nr. Model No.	Größe / Size cm / inch	Modellierdatum Sculpting Date	
480	10 / 4.00	1987	OE

Hum 480
Hosianna · Hosanna

Modell-Nr. Model No.	Größe / Size cm / inch	Modellierdatum Sculpting Date	
481	8,5 / 3.25	1987	CE

Anmerkung/Note:

Jahres-Christbaumschmuck 1989.

Annual Collectible Ornament 1989.

Hum 481
Viel Glück · Love From Above

OE: Offene Edition / Open Edition
CE: Produktion beendet / Closed Edition
TWD: Vorübergehend nicht mehr in Produktion / Temporarily withdrawn from production

Hum 482
Herrgottsblümchen
One For You, One For Me

Modell-Nr. Model No.	Größe / Size cm / inch	Modellierdatum Sculpting Date	
482/5/0	5 / 2.00	1991	CE
482/2/0	8 / 3.25	1987	OE

Editionen mit Sonderbodenbild/ Editions with special backstamp:

Modell-Nr. Model No.	Ausgabejahr Year	Ausgabeort Country	
482/5/0	1998	"Pen Pals" USA	CE

Hum 483
Sei nicht bang · I'll Protect Him

Modell-Nr. Model No.	Größe / Size cm / inch	Modellierdatum Sculpting Date	
483	9,5 / 3.75	1987	OE

Hum 484
Vom Himmel hoch · Peace On Earth

Modell-Nr. Model No.	Größe / Size cm / inch	Modellierdatum Sculpting Date	
484	10/ 4.00	1987	CE

Anmerkung/Note:

Jahres-Christbaumschmuck 1990.

Annual Collectible Ornament 1990.

OE: Offene Edition / Open Edition
CE: Produktion beendet / Closed Edition
TWD: Vorübergehend nicht mehr in Produktion / Temporarily withdrawn from production

Hum 485
Aus Nachbars Garten
Gift From A Friend

Modell-Nr. Model No.	Größe / Size cm / inch	Modellierdatum Sculpting Date	
485	12,5 / 5.00	1987	CE

Anmerkung/Note:

Exklusive Jahresedition für M.I.Hummel Clubmitglieder für das Clubjahr 1991/1992.

Exclusive Annual Edition for members of the M.I.Hummel Club in Club Year 1991/1992.

Hum 486
Schluß für heute · I Wonder

Modell-Nr. Model No.	Größe / Size cm / inch	Modellierdatum Sculpting Date	
486	13 / 5.25	1987	CE

Anmerkung/Note:

Exklusive Jahresedition für M.I.Hummel Clubmitglieder für das Clubjahr 1990/1991.

Exclusive Annual Edition for members of the M.I.Hummel Club in Club Year 1990/1991.

Hum 487
Sturmläuten · Let's Tell The World

Modell-Nr. Model No.	Größe / Size cm / inch	Modellierdatum Sculpting Date	
487	26 / 10.25	1987	CE

Anmerkung/Note:

Fünfte Figur der "Century Collection" im Jahre 1990, deren Produktion auf ein Jahr im 20. Jahrhundert beschränkt war. Ein spezieller Sonderbodenstempel und ein Zertifikat bestätigten die Zugehörigkeit zur Serie.

Fifth figurine in the "Century Collection" in 1990, which was produced for this one year only in the twentieth century. This was attested by a certifitate of authenticity and a special backstamp on the bottom of the figurines.

OE: Offene Edition / Open Edition
CE: Produktion beendet / Closed Edition
TWD: Vorübergehend nicht mehr in Produktion / Temporarily withdrawn from production

Modell-Nr. Model No.	Größe / Size cm / inch	Modellierdatum Sculpting Date	
488	10 / 4.00	1988	TWD

Anmerkung/Note:

Exklusive Sonderedition für M.I.Hummel Clubmitglieder für das Clubjahr 1997/1998.

Exclusive Preview Edition for members of the M.I.Hummel Club in Club Year 1997/1998.

Hum 488
Was ist das? · What's That?

Modell-Nr. Model No.	Größe / Size cm / inch	Modellierdatum Sculpting Date	
489	9 / 3.50	1988	OE

Anmerkung/Note:

Erste Ausgabe 1996 mit Sonderbodenbild im ersten Produktionsjahr.

First Issue 1996 with special backstamp in the first year of production.

Hum 489
Ich hab's nicht! · Pretty Please

Modell-Nr. Model No.	Größe / Size cm / inch	Modellierdatum Sculpting Date	
490	9 / 3.50	1988	OE

Anmerkung/Note:

Erste Ausgabe 1997 mit Sonderbodenbild im ersten Produktionsjahr.

First Issue 1997 with special backstamp in the first year of production.

Hum 490
Der Nichtstuer · Carefree

OE: Offene Edition / Open Edition
CE: Produktion beendet / Closed Edition
TWD: Vorübergehend nicht mehr in Produktion / Temporarily withdrawn from production

Modell-Nr. Model No.	Größe / Size cm / inch	Modellierdatum Sculpting Date	
493	10 / 4.00	1988	CE

Anmerkung/Note:

Exklusive Verlängerungsfigur für M.I.Hummel Clubmitglieder für das Clubjahr 1991/92.

Exclusive Renewal Figurine for members of the M.I.Hummel Club in the Club Year 1991/92.

Hum 493
Rechts oder links · Two Hands, One Treat

Modell-Nr. Model No.	Größe / Size cm / inch	Modellierdatum Sculpting Date	
495	10 / 4.00	1988	OE

Editionen mit Sonderbodenbild/ Editions with special backstamp:

Modell-Nr. Model No.	Ausgabejahr Year	Ausgabeland Country	
495	1996	"125th Anniversary" USA	CE

Anmerkung/Note:

Erste Ausgabe 1992 mit Sonderbodenbild im ersten Produktionsjahr.

First Issue 1992 with special backstamp in the first year of production.

Hum 495
Abendgebet · Evening Prayer

Modell-Nr. Model No.	Größe / Size cm / inch	Modellierdatum Sculpting Date	
498	10 / 4.00	1988	CE

Limitierte Ausgabe "Ich freu' mich so" 1997

Auf 25.000 Stück weltweit limitiert und einzeln nummeriert.

Produktion beendet.

Limited Edition "All Smiles" 1997

Worldwide limited and numbered edition of 25,000 pcs.

Closed Edition.

Hum 498
Ich freu' mich so · All Smiles

OE: Offene Edition / Open Edition
CE: Produktion beendet / Closed Edition
TWD: Vorübergehend nicht mehr in Produktion / Temporarily withdrawn from production

Modell-Nr. Model No.	Größe / Size cm / inch	Modellierdatum Sculpting Date	
512/A-E	20 / 8.00	1986	TWD

Hum 512
Geborgen (Mädchen) · Umbrella Girl
Porzellanpuppe · Porcelain Doll

Modell-Nr. Model No.	Größe / Size cm / inch	Modellierdatum Sculpting Date	
513/A-E	36 / 14.25	1988	TWD

Hum 513
Geigerlein · Little Fiddler
Porzellanpuppe · Porcelain Doll

Modell-Nr. Model No.	Größe / Size cm / inch	Modellierdatum Sculpting Date	
514/A-C	19 / 7.50	1988	TWD

Hum 514
Die Heuschrecke · Friend Or Foe?
Porzellanpuppe · Porcelain Doll

OE: Offene Edition / Open Edition
CE: Produktion beendet / Closed Edition
TWD: Vorübergehend nicht mehr in Produktion / Temporarily withdrawn from production

Modell-Nr. Model No.	Größe / Size cm / inch	Modellierdatum Sculpting Date	
516/A-E	37 / 14.50	1988	TWD

Hum 516
Wanderbub · Merry Wanderer
Porzellanpuppe · Porcelain Doll

Modell-Nr. Model No.	Größe / Size cm / inch	Modellierdatum Sculpting Date	
517A-C	37 / 14.50	1988	TWD

Hum 517
Gänseliesl · Goose Girl
Porzellanpuppe · Porcelain Doll

Modell-Nr. Model No.	Größe / Size cm / inch	Modellierdatum Sculpting Date	
518/A-E	24 / 9.50	1989	TWD

Hum 518
Geborgen (Junge) · Umbrella Boy
Porzellanpuppe · Porcelain Doll

OE: Offene Edition / Open Edition
CE: Produktion beendet / Closed Edition
TWD: Vorübergehend nicht mehr in Produktion / Temporarily withdrawn from production

Modell-Nr. Model No.	Größe / Size cm / inch	Modellierdatum Sculpting Date	
519/A-F	33 / 13.00	1989	TWD

Hum 519
Fahrt in die Weihnacht
Ride Into Christmas
Porzellanpuppe · Porcelain Doll

Modell-Nr. Model No.	Größe / Size cm / inch	Modellierdatum Sculpting Date	
521/A-E	34 / 13.50	1993	TWD

Hum 521
Erster Schulgang · School Girl
Porzellanpuppe · Porcelain Doll

Modell-Nr. Model No.	Größe / Size cm / inch	Modellierdatum Sculpting Date	
522/A-E	37 / 14.50	1995	TWD

Hum 522
Erster Schulgang · Little Scholar
Porzellanpuppe · Porcelain Doll

OE: Offene Edition / Open Edition
CE: Produktion beendet / Closed Edition
TWD: Vorübergehend nicht mehr in Produktion / Temporarily withdrawn from production

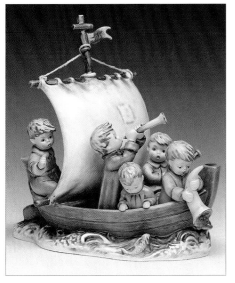

Modell-Nr. Model No.	Größe / Size cm / inch	Modellierdatum Sculpting Date	
530	23 / 9.00	1988	CE

Sonderausgabe "Land in Sicht" 1992

Auf 30.000 Stück weltweit limitiert und einzeln nummeriert.

Produktion beendet.

Special Commemorative Edition "Land In Sight" 1992

Worldwide limited and numbered edition of 30,000 pcs.

Closed Edition.

Hum 530
Land in Sicht · Land In Sight

Modell-Nr. Model No.	Größe / Size cm / inch	Modellierdatum Sculpting Date	
533	7,5 / 3.00	1988	OE

Editionen mit Sonderbodenbild/ Editions with special backstamp:

Modell-Nr. Model No.	Ausgabejahr Year	Ausgabeland Country	
533	1995	"Special Event" USA	CE

Anmerkung/Note:

Erste Ausgabe 1995 mit Sonderbodenbild im ersten Produktionsjahr.

First Issue 1995 with special backstamp in the first year of production.

Hum 533
Oh weh, mein Zahn! · Ooh, My Tooth

Modell-Nr. Model No.	Größe / Size cm / inch	Modellierdatum Sculpting Date	
534	6 / 2.50	1988	OE

Anmerkung/Note:

Erste Ausgabe 1991 mit Sonderbodenbild im ersten Produktionsjahr.

First Issue 1991 with special backstamp in the first year of production.

Hum 534
Nickerchen · A Nap

OE: Offene Edition / Open Edition
CE: Produktion beendet / Closed Edition
TWD: Vorübergehend nicht mehr in Produktion / Temporarily withdrawn from production

Hum 541
Selbst gebacken · Sweet As Can Be

Modell-Nr. Model No.	Größe / Size cm / inch	Modellierdatum Sculpting Date	
541	10 / 4.00	1988	OE seit / since 1998

Anmerkung/Note:

Exklusive Sonderedition für M.I.Hummel Clubmitglieder für das Clubjahr 1993/1994.

Exclusive Preview Edition for members of the M.I.Hummel Club in Club Year 1993/1994.

Hum 545
Bleib nicht so lange fort · Come Back Soon

Modell-Nr. Model No.	Größe / Size cm / inch	Modellierdatum Sculpting Date	
545	11 / 4.25	1988	OE

Anmerkung/Note:

Erste Ausgabe 1995 mit Sonderbodenbild im ersten Produktionsjahr.

First Issue 1995 with special backstamp in the first year of production.

Hum 548
Blumenmadl · Flower Girl

Modell-Nr. Model No.	Größe / Size cm / inch	Modellierdatum Sculpting Date	
548	11 / 4.25	1988	CE seit / since 2000

Anmerkung/Note:

Treuefigur für Mitglieder des M.I.Hummel Club, die in ihrem fünften, persönlichen Mitgliedsjahr sind.

Loyalty figurine for members of the M.I.Hummel Club in their 5th personal membership year.

OE: Offene Edition / Open Edition
CE: Produktion beendet / Closed Edition
TWD: Vorübergehend nicht mehr in Produktion / Temporarily withdrawn from production

Modell-Nr. Model No.	Größe / Size cm / inch	Modellierdatum Sculpting Date	
549/3/0	9 / 3.50	1992	CE
549/0	12 / 4.75	1988	-------------

Hum 549
Ein süßer Trost · A Sweet Offering

Anmerkung/Note:

549/3/0 Exklusive Verlängerungsfigur für M.I.Hummel Clubmitglieder für
das Clubjahr 1993/94.

Exclusive Renewal Figurine for members of the M.I.Hummel Club
in the Club Year 1993/94.

549/0 noch nicht veröffentlicht. Possible Future Edition.

Modell-Nr. Model No.	Größe / Size cm / inch	Modellierdatum Sculpting Date	
553	9 / 3.50	1988	OE

Editionen mit Sonderbodenbild/ Editions with special backstamp:

Modell-Nr. Model No.	Ausgabejahr Year	Ausgabeland Country	
553	1998	"Budapest" Ungarn, Hungary	CE

Hum 553
Spitzbub · Scamp

Anmerkung/Note:

Erste Ausgabe 1992 mit Sonderbodenbild im ersten Produktionsjahr.

First Issue 1992 with special backstamp in the first year of production.

Modell-Nr. Model No.	Größe / Size cm / inch	Modellierdatum Sculpting Date	
554	10,5 / 4.25	1988	OE seit / since 1998

Anmerkung/Note:

Exklusive Sonderedition für M.I.Hummel Clubmitglieder für das Clubjahr 1992/1993.

Exclusive Preview Edition for members of the M.I.Hummel Club in Club Year 1992/1993.

Hum 554
Frechdachs · Checky Fellow

OE: Offene Edition / Open Edition
CE: Produktion beendet / Closed Edition
TWD: Vorübergehend nicht mehr in Produktion / Temporarily withdrawn from production

Modell-Nr. Model No.	Größe / Size cm / inch	Modellierdatum Sculpting Date	
555	10 / 4.00	1988	TWD

Hum 555
Eins, zwei, drei · One, Two, Three

Anmerkung/Note:

Exklusive Sonderedition für M.I.Hummel Clubmitglieder für das Clubjahr 1996/1997.

Exclusive Preview Edition for members of the M.I.Hummel Club in Club Year 1996/1997.

Modell-Nr. Model No.	Größe / Size cm / inch	Modellierdatum Sculpting Date	
556	10 / 4.00	1988	OE

Editionen mit Sonderbodenbild/ Editions with special backstamp:

Modell-Nr. Model No.	Ausgabejahr Year	Ausgabeland Country	
556	1993	"Special Event" USA	CE
556	1998	"M.I.Hummelfest in Hessen" Deutschland, Germany	CE

Hum 556
Eins und eins... · One Plus One...

Anmerkung/Note:

Erste Ausgabe 1993 mit Sonderbodenbild im ersten Produktionsjahr.

First Issue 1993 with special backstamp in the first year of production.

Modell-Nr. Model No.	Größe / Size cm / inch	Modellierdatum Sculpting Date	
557	10 / 4.00	1989	OE seit / since 1998

Anmerkung/Note:

Exklusive Sonderedition für M.I.Hummel Clubmitglieder für das Clubjahr 1995/1996.

Exclusive Preview Edition for members of the M.I.Hummel Club in Club Year 1995/1996.

Hum 557
Mit Sang und Klang · Strum Along

OE: Offene Edition / Open Edition
CE: Produktion beendet / Closed Edition
TWD: Vorübergehend nicht mehr in Produktion / Temporarily withdrawn from production

Modell-Nr. Model No.	Größe / Size cm / inch	Modellierdatum Sculpting Date		
558	10,5 / 4.25	1988		OE seit / since 1998

Hum 558
Der kleine Troubadour
The Little Troubadour

Anmerkung/Note:

Exklusive Sonderedition für M.I.Hummel Clubmitglieder für das Clubjahr 1994/1995.

Exclusive Preview Edition for members of the M.I.Hummel Club in Club Year 1994/1995.

Modell-Nr. Model No.	Größe / Size cm / inch	Modellierdatum Sculpting Date	
559	9,5 / 3.75	1988	OE

Hum 559
Sicher ist sicher · Heart And Soul

Anmerkung/Note:

Erste Ausgabe 1996 mit Sonderbodenbild im ersten Produktionsjahr.

First Issue 1996 with special backstamp in the first year of production.

Modell-Nr. Model No.	Größe / Size cm / inch	Modellierdatum Sculpting Date	
560	10 / 4.00	1988	CE

Hum 560
Ein fröhlicher Gesell · Lucky Fellow

Anmerkung/Note:

Exklusive Verlängerungsfigur für M.I.Hummel Clubmitglieder
für das Clubjahr 1992/93.

Exclusive Renewal Figurine for members of the M.I.Hummel Club
in the Club Year 1992/93.

OE: Offene Edition / Open Edition
CE: Produktion beendet / Closed Edition
TWD: Vorübergehend nicht mehr in Produktion / Temporarily withdrawn from production

Hum 561
Großmutter wartet · Grandma's Girl

Modell-Nr. Model No.	Größe / Size cm / inch	Modellierdatum Sculpting Date	
561	10 / 4.00	1988	OE

Editionen mit Sonderbodenbild/ Editions with special backstamp:

Modell-Nr. Model No.	Ausgabejahr Year	Ausgabeland Country	
561	1993	"M.I.Hummel Club Convention" USA	CE
561	1997	"Heiligenkreuz" Österreich, Austria	CE

Anmerkung/Note:

Erste Ausgabe 1991 mit Sonderbodenbild im ersten Produktionsjahr.

First Issue 1991 with special backstamp in the first year of production.

Hum 562
Großvater wartet · Grandpa's Boy

Modell-Nr. Model No.	Größe / Size cm / inch	Modellierdatum Sculpting Date	
562	10,5 / 4.25	1988	OE

Editionen mit Sonderbodenbild/ Editions with special backstamp:

Modell-Nr. Model No.	Ausgabejahr Year	Ausgabeland Country	
562	1993	"M.I.Hummel Club Convention" USA	CE
562	1997	"Heiligenkreuz" Österreich, Austria	CE

Anmerkung/Note:

Erste Ausgabe 1991 mit Sonderbodenbild im ersten Produktionsjahr.

First Issue 1991 with special backstamp in the first year of production.

Hum 563
Kleine Besucherin · Little Visitor

Modell-Nr. Model No.	Größe / Size cm / inch	Modellierdatum Sculpting Date	
563/3/0	10 / 4.00	1988	-------------
563/0	13 / 5.25	1991	CE

Anmerkung/Note:

563/3/0 Noch nicht veröffentlicht. Possible Future Edition.

563/0 Exklusive Jahresedition für M.I.Hummel Clubmitglieder für
    das Clubjahr 1994/1995.

    Exclusive Annual Edition for members of the M.I.Hummel Club
    in Club Year 1994/1995.

OE: Offene Edition / Open Edition
CE: Produktion beendet / Closed Edition
TWD: Vorübergehend nicht mehr in Produktion / Temporarily withdrawn from production

Modell-Nr. Model No.	Größe / Size cm / inch	Modellierdatum Sculpting Date	
564	9 / 3.50	1988	OE

Hum 564
Ich mag nicht · Free Spirit

Anmerkung/Note:

Erste Ausgabe 1997 mit Sonderbodenbild im ersten Produktionsjahr.

First Issue 1997 with special backstamp in the first year of production.

Modell-Nr. Model No.	Größe / Size cm / inch	Modellierdatum Sculpting Date	
566	15 / 6.00	1988	OE

Hum 566
Der Angler · The Angler

Anmerkung/Note:

Erste Ausgabe 1995 mit Sonderbodenbild im ersten Produktionsjahr.

First Issue 1995 with special backstamp in the first year of production.

Modell-Nr. Model No.	Größe / Size cm / inch	Modellierdatum Sculpting Date	
569	12 / 4.75	1988	OE

Editionen mit Sonderbodenbild/ Editions with special backstamp:

Modell-Nr. Model No.	Ausgabejahr Year	Ausgabeland Country	
569	1997	"Canada - 130 years" Kanada	CE
569	1998	Deutschland, Germany	CE

Hum 569
Freifahrt Zeppelin · A Free Flight

Anmerkung/Note:

Erste Ausgabe 1993 mit Sonderbodenbild im ersten Produktionsjahr.

First Issue 1993 with special backstamp in the first year of production.

Hum 571
Laternenengel · Angelic Guide

Modell-Nr. Model No.	Größe / Size cm / inch	Modellierdatum Sculpting Date	
571	9 / 3.50	1989	CE

Anmerkung/Note:

Jahres-Christbaumschmuck 1991.

Annual Collectible Ornament 1991.

Hum 574
Das Nesthäckchen · Rock-A-Bye

Modell-Nr. Model No.	Größe / Size cm / inch	Modellierdatum Sculpting Date	
574	19 / 7.50	1989	CE

Anmerkung/Note:

Neunte Figur der "Century Collection" im Jahre 1994, deren Produktion auf ein Jahr im 20. Jahrhundert beschränkt war. Ein spezieller Sonderbodenstempel und ein Zertifikat bestätigten die Zugehörigkeit zur Serie.

Ninth figurine in the "Century Collection" in 1994, which was produced for this one year only in the twentieth century. This was attested by a certifitate of authenticity and a special backstamp on the bottom of the figurine.

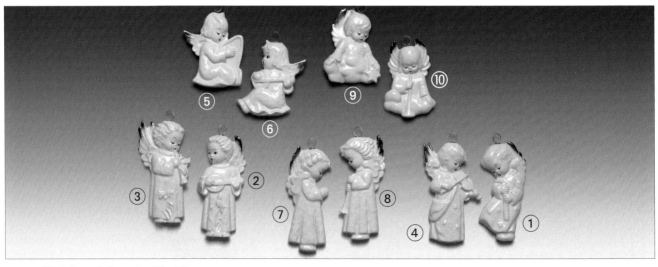

Christbaumbehang (weiß/gold)
Christmas Ornaments (white/gold)

OE: Offene Edition / Open Edition
CE: Produktion beendet / Closed Edition
TWD: Vorübergehend nicht mehr in Produktion / Temporarily withdrawn from production

Christbaumbehang
Christmas Ornaments

	Modell-Nr. Model No.	Größe / Size cm / inch	Modellierdatum Sculpting Date		
①	Hum 575	8 / 3.25	1987	TWD	Christkindlein kommt Heavenly Angel
②	Hum 576	8 / 3.25	1988	TWD	Adventsengel (mit Mandoline) Festival Harmony (Mandolin)
③	Hum 577	8 / 3.25	1988	TWD	Adventsengel (mit Flöte) Festival Harmony (Flute)
④	Hum 578	8,5 / 3.50	1988	TWD	Himmlische Klänge Celestial Musician
⑤	Hum 579	6 / 2.50	1988	TWD	Lobgesang Song Of Praise
⑥	Hum 580	6 / 2.50	1988	TWD	Engel mit Laute Angel With Lute
⑦	Hum 581	9 / 3.50	1988	TWD	Dankgebet Prayer Of Thanks
⑧	Hum 582	9 / 3.50	1988	TWD	Leise Töne Gentle Song
⑨	Hum 585	6,5 / 2.75	1988	TWD	Engel auf Wolke Angel In Cloud
⑩	Hum 586	6,5 / 2.75	1988	TWD	Engel mit Trompete Angel With Trumpet

OE: Offene Edition / Open Edition
CE: Produktion beendet / Closed Edition
TWD: Vorübergehend nicht mehr in Produktion / Temporarily withdrawn from production

Modell-Nr. Model No.	Größe / Size cm / inch	Modellierdatum Sculpting Date	
596	8 / 3.25	1995	OE

Hum 596
Dankgebet · Thanksgiving Prayer
Weihnachtsschmuck Christmas Ornament

Anmerkung/Note:

Erste Ausgabe 1997 mit Sonderbodenbild im ersten Produktionsjahr.

First Issue 1997 with special backstamp in the first year of production.

Modell-Nr. Model No.	Größe / Size cm / inch	Modellierdatum Sculpting Date	
597	8 / 3.25	1995	OE

Hum 597
Leise Töne · Echoes Of Joy
Weihnachtsschmuck Christmas Ornament

Anmerkung/Note:

Erste Ausgabe 1998 mit Sonderbodenbild im ersten Produktionsjahr.

First Issue 1998 with special backstamp in the first year of production.

Modell-Nr. Model No.	Größe / Size cm / inch	Modellierdatum Sculpting Date	
598	7 / 2.75	1996	OE

Anmerkung/Note:

Erste Ausgabe 1999 mit Sonderbodenbild im ersten Produktionsjahr.

First Issue 1999 with special backstamp in the first year of production.

Hum 598
Festliche Trompetenklänge · A Joyful Noise
Weihnachtsschmuck Christmas Ornament

OE: Offene Edition / Open Edition
CE: Produktion beendet / Closed Edition
TWD: Vorübergehend nicht mehr in Produktion / Temporarily withdrawn from production

Modell-Nr. Model No.	Größe / Size cm / inch	Modellierdatum Sculpting Date	
599	7 / 2.75	1996	OE

Hum 599
Ich leuchte Dir den Weg · Light The Way
Weihnachtsschmuck Christmas Ornament

Anmerkung/Note:

Erste Ausgabe 2000 mit Sonderbodenbild im ersten Produktionsjahr.

First Issue 2000 with special backstamp in the first year of production.

Modell-Nr. Model No.	Größe / Size cm / inch	Modellierdatum Sculpting Date	
600	21 / 8.25	1989	CE

Hum 600
Wir wünschen Dir das Beste
We Wish You The Best

Anmerkung/Note:

Sechste Figur der "Century Collection" im Jahre 1991, deren Produktion auf ein Jahr im 20. Jahrhundert beschränkt war. Ein spezieller Sonderbodenstempel und ein Zertifikat bestätigten die Zugehörigkeit zur Serie.

Sixth figurine in the "Century Collection" in 1991, which was produced for this one year only in the twentieth century. This was attested by a certifitate of authenticity and a special backstamp on the bottom of the figurine.

Modell-Nr. Model No.	Größe / Size cm / inch	Modellierdatum Sculpting Date	
608	8 / 3.25	1989	OE

Anmerkung/Note:

Erste Ausgabe 1996 mit Sonderbodenbild im ersten Produktionsjahr.

First Issue 1996 with special backstamp in the first year of production.

OE: Offene Edition / Open Edition
CE: Produktion beendet / Closed Edition
TWD: Vorübergehend nicht mehr in Produktion / Temporarily withdrawn from production

Hum 608
Enziankind · Blossom Time

Hum IV/608
Enziankind · Blossom Time
Musikdose · Music Box

Modell-Nr. Model No.	Größe / Size cm / inch	Modellierdatum Sculpting Date	
IV/608	14,5 / 5.75	1998	CE

Anmerkung/Note:

Limitierte Ausgabe für das Hummel Museum in New Braunfels.

Limited Edition for the Hummel Museum in New Braunfels.

Hum 615
Erste Begegnung · Private Conversation

Modell-Nr. Model No.	Größe / Size cm / inch	Modellierdatum Sculpting Date	
615	11,5 / 4.50	1989	CE

Anmerkung/Note:

Exklusive Jahresedition für M.I.Hummel Clubmitglieder für das Clubjahr 1999/2000.

Exclusive Annual Edition for members of the M.I.Hummel Club in Club Year 1999/2000.

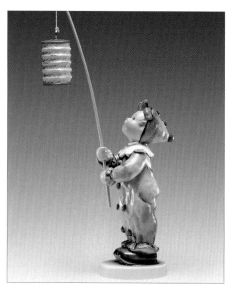

Hum 616
Laterne, Laterne... · Parade Of Lights

Modell-Nr. Model No.	Größe / Size cm / inch	Modellierdatum Sculpting Date	
616	15,5 / 6.25	1989	OE

Anmerkung/Note:

Erste Ausgabe 1993 mit Sonderbodenbild im ersten Produktionsjahr.

First Issue 1993 with special backstamp in the first year of production.

OE: Offene Edition / Open Edition
CE: Produktion beendet / Closed Edition
TWD: Vorübergehend nicht mehr in Produktion / Temporarily withdrawn from production

Modell-Nr. Model No.	Größe / Size cm / inch	Modellierdatum Sculpting Date	
620	21 / 8.25	1989	CE

Anmerkung/Note:

Exclusives Angebot für alle M.I.Hummel Clubmitglieder im Jahr 1995.

Auf 10.000 Stück weltweit limitiert und einzeln nummeriert.

Exclusive Offer for all members of the M.I.Hummel Club in 1995.

Worldwide limited and numbered edition of 10,000 pcs.

Hum 620
Großmutter erzählt
A Story From Grandma

Modell-Nr. Model No.	Größe / Size cm / inch	Modellierdatum Sculpting Date	
621	22 / 8.75	1989	CE

Anmerkung/Note:

Exclusives Angebot für alle M.I.Hummel Clubmitglieder im Jahr 1994.

Auf 10.000 Stück weltweit limitiert und einzeln nummeriert.

Exclusive Offer for all members of the M.I.Hummel Club in 1994.

Worldwide limited and numbered edition of 10,000 pcs.

Hum 621
Beim Großvaterle · At Grandpa's

Modell-Nr. Model No.	Größe / Size cm / inch	Modellierdatum Sculpting Date	
622	8,5 / 3.25	1989	CE

Anmerkung/Note:

Jahres-Christbaumschmuck 1992.

Annual Collectible Ornament 1992.

Hum 622
Wir zünden froh die Kerzen an
Light Up The Night

OE: Offene Edition / Open Edition
CE: Produktion beendet / Closed Edition
TWD: Vorübergehend nicht mehr in Produktion / Temporarily withdrawn from production

Modell-Nr. Model No.	Größe / Size cm / inch	Modellierdatum Sculpting Date	
623	11,5 / 4.50	1989	CE

Hum 623
Friede den Menschen · Herald On High

Anmerkung/Note:

Jahres-Christbaumschmuck 1993.

Annual Collectible Ornament 1993.

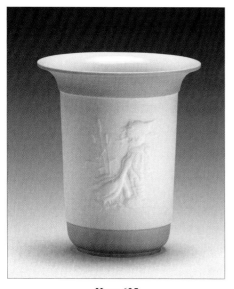

Modell-Nr. Model No.	Größe / Size cm / inch	Modellierdatum Sculpting Date	
625	10 / 4.00	1998	TWD

Hum 625
Gänseliesl · Goose Girl
Vase · Vase

Anmerkung/Note:

Diese Vase wurde 1997 nur in den USA angeboten.

This Vase was offered in 1997 in the US only.

Modell-Nr. Model No.	Größe / Size cm / inch	Modellierdatum Sculpting Date	
626	14 / 5.50	1991	CE

Anmerkung/Note:

Exklusive Jahresedition für M.I.Hummel Clubmitglieder für das Clubjahr 1993/1994.

Exclusive Annual Edition for members of the M.I.Hummel Club in Club Year 1993/1994.

Hum 626
Ich war's nicht · I Didn't Do It

OE: Offene Edition / Open Edition
CE: Produktion beendet / Closed Edition
TWD: Vorübergehend nicht mehr in Produktion / Temporarily withdrawn from production

Modell-Nr. Model No.	Größe / Size cm / inch	Modellierdatum Sculpting Date	
628	14,5 / 5.75	1992	CE

UNICEF Sonderausgabe

Auf 25.000 Stück weltweit limitiert und einzeln nummeriert.

Produktion beendet.

UNICEF Special Edition

Worldwide limited and numbered edition of 25,000 pcs.

Closed Edition.

Hum 628
Eine für mich und eine für dich
Gentle Fellowship

Modell-Nr. Model No.	Größe / Size cm / inch	Modellierdatum Sculpting Date	
629	9 / 3.50	1992	CE

Anmerkung/Note:

Exklusive Verlängerungsfigur für M.I.Hummel Clubmitglieder für das Clubjahr 1995/96.

Exclusive Renewal Figurine for members of the M.I.Hummel Club in the Club Years 1995/96.

Hum 629
Jungbäuerin · From Me To You

Modell-Nr. Model No.	Größe / Size cm / inch	Modellierdatum Sculpting Date	
630	9 / 3.50	1992	CE

Anmerkung/Note:

Exklusive Verlängerungsfigur für M.I.Hummel Clubmitglieder für das Clubjahr 1994/95.

Exclusive Renewal Figurine for members of the M.I.Hummel Club in the Club Year 1994/95.

Hum 630
Jungbauer · For Keeps

OE: Offene Edition / Open Edition
CE: Produktion beendet / Closed Edition
TWD: Vorübergehend nicht mehr in Produktion / Temporarily withdrawn from production

Modell-Nr. Model No.	Größe / Size cm / inch	Modellierdatum Sculpting Date	
632	9 / 3.50	1990	CE

Hum 632
Ich spiel' gern Ball · At Play

Anmerkung/Note:

Exklusive Jahresedition für M.I.Hummel Clubmitglieder für das Clubjahr 1998/1999.

Exclusive Annual Edition for members of the M.I.Hummel Club in Club Year 1998/1999.

Modell-Nr. Model No.	Größe / Size cm / inch	Modellierdatum Sculpting Date	
633	12 / 4.75	1990	OE

Hum 633
Was frag' ich viel nach Geld und Gut...
I'm Carefree

Anmerkung/Note:

Erste Ausgabe 1994 mit Sonderbodenbild im ersten Produktionsjahr.

First Issue 1994 with special backstamp in the first year of production.

Modell-Nr. Model No.	Größe / Size cm / inch	Modellierdatum Sculpting Date	
634/2/0	11,5 / 4.50	1990	OE
634/I	15 / 6.00	1990	-------------

Hum 634
Sauwetter · Sunshower

Anmerkung/Note:

634/2/0 Erste Ausgabe 1997 mit Sonderbodenbild im ersten Produktionsjahr.

First Issue 1997 with special backstamp in the first year of production.

634/I Noch nicht veröffentlicht. Possible Future Edition.

OE: Offene Edition / Open Edition
CE: Produktion beendet / Closed Edition
TWD: Vorübergehend nicht mehr in Produktion / Temporarily withdrawn from production

Modell-Nr. Model No.	Größe / Size cm / inch	Modellierdatum Sculpting Date	
635	31 / 12.50	1990	CE

Hum 635
Frühlingstanz · Welcome Spring

Anmerkung/Note:

Achte Figur der "Century Collection" im Jahre 1993, deren Produktion auf ein Jahr im 20. Jahrhundert beschränkt war. Ein spezieller Sonderbodenstempel und ein Zertifikat bestätigten die Zugehörigkeit zur Serie.

Eighth figurine in the "Century Collection" in 1993, which was produced for this one year only in the twentieth century. This was attested by a certifitate of authenticity and a special backstamp on the bottom of the figurine.

Modell-Nr. Model No.	Größe / Size cm / inch	Modellierdatum Sculpting Date	
638	10 / 4.00	1997	TWD

Hum 638
Enzian-Mädchen · The Botanist
Vase · Vase

Anmerkung/Note:

Diese Vase wurde 1998 nur in den USA angeboten.
This Vase was offered in 1998 in the US only.

Modell-Nr. Model No.	Größe / Size cm / inch	Modellierdatum Sculpting Date	
641/4/0	9 / 3.50	1995	OE
641/0	12 / 4.75	1990	OE

641/0

Hum 641
Dankgebet · Thanksgiving Prayer

Anmerkung/Note:

641/4/0, 641/0 Erste Ausgabe 1997 mit Sonderbodenbild im ersten Produktionsjahr.
First Issue 1997 with special backstamp in the first year of production.

641/4/0

Modell-Nr. Model No.	Größe / Size cm / inch	Modellierdatum Sculpting Date	
642/4/0	9 / 3.50	1996	OE
642/0	12,5 / 5.00	1990	OE

642/4/0

Anmerkung/Note:

642/4/0, 642/0 Erste Ausgabe 1998 mit Sonderbodenbild im ersten Produktionsjahr.

First Issue 1998 with special backstamp in the first year of production.

Hum 642
Leise Töne · Echoes Of Joy

Modell-Nr. Model No.	Größe / Size cm / inch	Modellierdatum Sculpting Date	
643/4/0	8 / 3.25	1996	OE
643/0	13 / 5.25	1990	OE

643/4/0

Anmerkung/Note:

643/4/0, 643/0 Erste Ausgabe 1999 mit Sonderbodenbild im ersten Produktionsjahr.

First Issue 1999 with special backstamp in the first year of production.

Hum 643
Festliche Trompetenklänge · A Joyful Noise

Modell-Nr. Model No.	Größe / Size cm / inch	Modellierdatum Sculpting Date	
645	8 / 3.25	1991	CE seit/ since 1999

Anmerkung/Note:

Erste Ausgabe 1996 mit Sonderbodenbild im ersten Produktionsjahr.

First Issue 1996 with special backstamp in the first year of production.

Hum 645
Weihnachtslied · Christmas Song
Weihnachtsschmuck Christmas Ornament

OE: Offene Edition / Open Edition
CE: Produktion beendet / Closed Edition
TWD: Vorübergehend nicht mehr in Produktion / Temporarily withdrawn from production

Modell-Nr. Model No.	Größe / Size cm / inch	Modellierdatum Sculpting Date	
646	7 / 2.75	1991	CE seit/ since 1999

Hum 646
Himmlische Klänge · Celestial Musician
Weihnachtsschmuck Christmas Ornament

Anmerkung/Note:

Erste Ausgabe 1993 mit Sonderbodenbild im ersten Produktionsjahr.

First Issue 1993 with special backstamp in the first year of production.

Modell-Nr. Model No.	Größe / Size cm / inch	Modellierdatum Sculpting Date	
647	7 / 2.75	1991	CE seit/ since 1999

Hum 647
Adventsengel mit Mandoline
Festival Harmony (Mandolin)
Weihnachtsschmuck · Christmas Ornament

Anmerkung/Note:

Erste Ausgabe 1994 mit Sonderbodenbild im ersten Produktionsjahr.

First Issue 1994 with special backstamp in the first year of production.

Modell-Nr. Model No.	Größe / Size cm / inch	Modellierdatum Sculpting Date	
648	7 / 2.75	1991	CE seit/ since 1999

Anmerkung/Note:

Erste Ausgabe 1995 mit Sonderbodenbild im ersten Produktionsjahr.

First Issue 1995 with special backstamp in the first year of production.

Hum 648
Adventsengel mit Flöte · Weihnachtsschmuck
Festival Harmony (Flute)
Christmas Ornament

OE: Offene Edition / Open Edition
CE: Produktion beendet / Closed Edition
TWD: Vorübergehend nicht mehr in Produktion / Temporarily withdrawn from production

Modell-Nr. Model No.	Größe / Size cm / inch	Modellierdatum Sculpting Date	
649/0	12 / 4.75	1990	CE
649/I	14 / 5.50	1996	------------

649/0 Limitierte Ausgabe "Ich kann's kaum erwarten" 1996

Auf 25.000 Stück weltweit limitiert und einzeln nummeriert.

Produktion beendet.

649/0 Limited Edition "Fascination" 1996

Worldwide limited and numbered edition of 25,000 pcs.

Closed Edition.

649/I Noch nicht veröffentlicht, Possible Future Edition.

Hum 649
Ich kann's kaum erwarten · Fascination

Modell-Nr. Model No.	Größe / Size cm / inch	Modellierdatum Sculpting Date	
658	9 / 3.50	1991	CE

Anmerkung/Note:

Exklusive Jahresedition für M.I.Hummel Clubmitglieder für das Clubjahr 1997/1998.

Exclusive Annual Edition for members of the M.I.Hummel Club in Club Year 1997/1998.

Hum 658
Behüt' uns beide · Playful Blessing

Modell-Nr. Model No.	Größe / Size cm / inch	Modellierdatum Sculpting Date	
660	17,5 / 6.75	1991	CE

Anmerkung/Note:

Zwölfte Figur der "Century Collection" im Jahre 1997, deren Produktion auf ein Jahr im 20. Jahrhundert beschränkt war. Ein spezieller Sonderbodenstempel und ein Zertifikat bestätigten die Zugehörigkeit zur Serie.

Twelfth figurine in the "Century Collection" in 1997, which was produced for this one year only in the twentieth century. This was attested by a certifitate of authenticity and a special backstamp on the bottom of the figurine.

OE: Offene Edition / Open Edition
CE: Produktion beendet / Closed Edition
TWD: Vorübergehend nicht mehr in Produktion / Temporarily withdrawn from production

Hum 660
Es wär' so schön gewesen · Fond Good-Bye

Modell-Nr. Model No.	Größe / Size cm / inch	Modellierdatum Sculpting Date	
662/0	11 / 4.25	1991	CE
662/I	15 / 6.00	1992	CE

662/0 UNICEF Sonderausgabe
662/0 UNICEF Special Edition

662/I UNICEF Sonderausgabe

Auf 25.000 Stück weltweit limitiert und einzeln nummeriert.

Produktion beendet.

662/I UNICEF Special Edition

Worldwide limited and numbered edition of 25,000 pcs.

Closed Edition.

Hum 662
Laß' uns zusammenstehen
Friends Together

Modell-Nr. Model No.	Größe / Size cm / inch	Modellierdatum Sculpting Date	
668	18,5 / 7.25	1992	CE

Anmerkung/Note:

Zehnte Figur der "Century Collection" im Jahre 1995, deren Produktion auf ein Jahr im 20. Jahrhundert beschränkt war. Ein spezieller Sonderbodenstempel und ein Zertifikat bestätigten die Zugehörigkeit zur Serie.

Tenth figurine in the "Century Collection" in 1995, which was produced for this one year only in the twentieth century. This was attested by a certifitate of authenticity and a special backstamp on the bottom of the figurine.

Hum 668
Viel Glück · Strike Up The Band

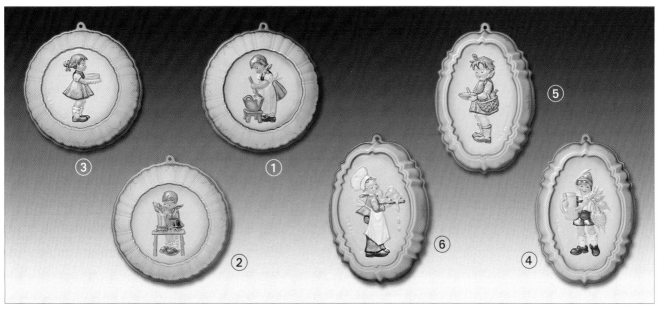

Küchenformen · Kitchen Molds

Modell-Nr. Model No.	Größe / Size cm / inch	Modellierdatum Sculpting Date		
① Hum 669	19 x 20 / 7.50 x 8.00	1989	TWD	Die Bäckerin, Baking Day
② Hum 670	19 x 20 / 7.50 x 8.00	1989	TWD	Der Kaufmann, A Fair Measure
③ Hum 671	19 x 20 / 7.50 x 8.00	1989	TWD	Selbst gebacken, Sweet As Can Be
④ Hum 672	15 x 22 / 6.00 x 8.75	1989	TWD	Rettichbub, For Father
⑤ Hum 673	15 x 22 / 6.00 x 8.75	1989	TWD	Für die Hungrigen, Supper's Coming
⑥ Hum 674	15 x 22 / 6.00 x 8.75	1989	TWD	Der kleine Konditor, Baker

Kerzenhalter · Candle Holder

Modell-Nr. Model No.	Größe / Size cm / inch	Modellierdatum Sculpting Date		
① Hum 676	17 / 6.75	1988	TWD	Frühling, Apple Tree Girl
② Hum 677	17 / 6.75	1988	TWD	Herbst, Apple Tree Boy
③ Hum 678	16 / 6.25	1989	TWD	Liebt mich, liebt mich nicht..., She Loves Me, She Loves Me Not...
④ Hum 679	16 / 6.25	1989	TWD	Freunde, Friends

OE: Offene Edition / Open Edition
CE: Produktion beendet / Closed Edition
TWD: Vorübergehend nicht mehr in Produktion / Temporarily withdrawn from production

Modell-Nr. Model No.	Größe / Size cm / inch	Modellierdatum Sculpting Date	
690	15 / 6.00	1977	CE

Hum 690
Gut beschirmt · Smiling Through
Plakette · Plaque

Anmerkung/Note:

Exklusive Jahresedition für M.I.Hummel Clubmitglieder für das Clubjahr 1978/1979.

Exclusive Annual Edition for members of the M.I.Hummel Club in Club Year 1978/1979.

Modell-Nr. Model No.	Größe / Size cm / inch	Modellierdatum Sculpting Date	
692	15 / 6.00	1994	CE

Anmerkung/Note:

Jahres Weihnachtsteller 1996.

Annual Christmas Plate 1996.

Hum 692
Weihnachtslied · Christmas Song

Modell-Nr. Model No.	Größe / Size cm / inch	Modellierdatum Sculpting Date	
693	15 / 6.00	1994	CE

Anmerkung/Note:

Jahres Weihnachtsteller 1995.

Annual Christmas Plate 1995.

Hum 693
Adventsengel mit Flöte
Festival Harmony (Flute)

OE: Offene Edition / Open Edition
CE: Produktion beendet / Closed Edition
TWD: Vorübergehend nicht mehr in Produktion / Temporarily withdrawn from production

Modell-Nr. Model No.	Größe / Size cm / inch	Modellierdatum Sculpting Date	
694	15 / 6.00	1995	CE

Anmerkung/Note:

Jahres Weihnachtsteller 1997.

Annual Christmas Plate 1997.

Hum 694
Dankgebet · Thanksgiving Prayer

Modell-Nr. Model No.	Größe / Size cm / inch	Modellierdatum Sculpting Date	
695	15 / 6.00	1995	CE

Anmerkung/Note:

Jahres Weihnachtsteller 1998.

Annual Christmas Plate 1998.

Hum 695
Leise Töne · Echoes Of Joy

Modell-Nr. Model No.	Größe / Size cm / inch	Modellierdatum Sculpting Date	
696	15 / 6.00	1996	CE

Anmerkung/Note:

Jahres Weihnachtsteller 1999.

Annual Christmas Plate 1999.

Hum 696
Festliche Trompetenklänge · A Joyful Noise

OE: Offene Edition / Open Edition
CE: Produktion beendet / Closed Edition
TWD: Vorübergehend nicht mehr in Produktion / Temporarily withdrawn from production

Modell-Nr. Model No.	Größe / Size cm / inch	Modellierdatum Sculpting Date	
697	15 / 6.00	1996	CE

Hum 697
Ich leuchte Dir den Weg · Light The Way

Anmerkung/Note:

Jahres Weihnachtsteller 2000.

Annual Christmas Plate 2000.

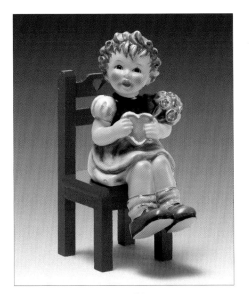

Modell-Nr. Model No.	Größe / Size cm / inch	Modellierdatum Sculpting Date	
698	12 / 4.75	1996	OE

Hum 698
I' mog Di' · Heart's Delight

Anmerkung/Note:

Erste Ausgabe 1998 mit Sonderbodenbild im ersten Produktionsjahr.

First Issue 1998 with special backstamp in the first year of production.

Mit Holzstuhl, red wooden chair included.

Modell-Nr. Model No.	Größe / Size cm / inch	Modellierdatum Sculpting Date	
699	12,5 / 5.00	1996	OE

Hum 699
Vielen Dank für alles · Love In Bloom

Anmerkung/Note:

Erste Ausgabe 1998 mit Sonderbodenbild im ersten Produktionsjahr.

First Issue 1998 with special backstamp in the first year of production.

Mit Holzwagen, Wooden waggon included.

OE: Offene Edition / Open Edition
CE: Produktion beendet / Closed Edition
TWD: Vorübergehend nicht mehr in Produktion / Temporarily withdrawn from production

Jahresglocken · Annual Bells

Modell-Nr. Model No.	Größe / Size cm / inch	Modellierdatum Sculpting Date		
Hum 700	15 / 6.00	1976	CE	Heini, Bandoneonspieler, Let's Sing
				Jahresglocke 1978, Annual Bell 1978
Hum701	15 / 6.00	1977	CE	Auf Wiedersehen, Farewell
				Jahresglocke 1979, Annual Bell 1979
Hum 702	15 / 6.00	1978	CE	Der Gelehrte, Thoughtful
				Jahresglocke 1980, Annual Bell 1980
Hum 703	15 / 6.00	1978	CE	Mach's nach, In Tune
				Jahresglocke 1981, Annual Bell 1981
Hum 704	15 / 6.00	1978	CE	Liebt mich, liebt mich nicht..., She Loves Me, She Loves Me Not...
				Jahresglocke 1982, Annual Bell 1982
Hum 705	15 / 6.00	1980	CE	Der erste Strumpf, Knit One
				Jahresglocke 1983, Annual Bell 1983
Hum 706	15 / 6.00	1980	CE	I' hab's erreicht, Mountaineer
				Jahresglocke 1984, Annual Bell 1984
Hum 707	15 / 6.00	1980	CE	Die kleine Sängerin, Girl With Sheet Music
				Jahresglocke 1985, Annual Bell 1985
Hum 708	15 / 6.00	1979	CE	Auf los geht's los, Sing Along
				Jahresglocke 1986, Annual Bell 1986
Hum 709	15 / 6.00	1983	CE	Ein dicker Gruß, With Loving Greetings
				Jahresglocke 1987, Annual Bell 1987
Hum 710	15 / 6.00	1983	CE	Musterschülerin, Busy Student
				Jahresglocke 1988, Annual Bell 1988
Hum 711	15 / 6.00	1983	CE	Das Allerneueste, Latest News
				Jahresglocke 1989, Annual Bell 1989
Hum 712	15 / 6.00	1983	CE	Was gibt's Neues?, What's New?
				Jahresglocke 1990, Annual Bell 1990
Hum 713	15 / 6.00	1988	CE	Osterüberraschung, Favorite Pet
				Jahresglocke 1991, Annual Bell 1991
Hum 714	15 / 6.00	1988	CE	Ein frohes Lied, Whistler's Duet
				Jahresglocke 1992, Annual Bell 1992

Hum 715
Ich leuchte Dir den Weg · Light The Way

Modell-Nr. Model No.	Größe / Size cm / inch	Modellierdatum Sculpting Date	
715/4/0	8 / 3.25	1995	OE
715/0	12,5 / 5.00	1995	OE

Anmerkung/Note:

Erste Ausgabe 2000 mit Sonderbodenbild im ersten Produktionsjahr.

First Issue 2000 with special backstamp in the first year of production.

715/4/0

Hum 717
I' hab' Di' gern · Valentine Gift
Aufstellschild · Plaque

Modell-Nr. Model No.	Größe / Size cm / inch	Modellierdatum Sculpting Date	
717	14 / 5.50	1995	CE

Anmerkung/Note:

Exklusive Sonderedition für M.I.Hummel Clubmitglieder für das Clubjahr 1996/1997.

Exclusive Special Edition for members of the M.I.Hummel Club in Club Year 1996/1997.

Hum 718/A-E, Hum 214

OE: Offene Edition / Open Edition
CE: Produktion beendet / Closed Edition
TWD: Vorübergehend nicht mehr in Produktion / Temporarily withdrawn from production

	Modell-Nr. Model No.	Größe / Size cm / inch	Modellierdatum Sculpting Date		
①	Hum 718/A	7 / 2.75	1996	OE	Ein Licht so hell und klar, Let It Shine
②	Hum 718/B	6,5 / 2.50	1996	OE	Schlaflied, Hush A Bye
③	Hum 718/C	7 / 2.75	1996	OE	Ein heller Schein, Holy Offering
④	Hum 718/D	7 / 2.75	1996	OE	Stimmt ein, Join In Song
⑤	Hum 718/E	6,5 / 2.50	1996	OE	Trompetensolo, Peaceful Sounds
⑥	Hum 214/D/O	7 / 2.75	1996	OE	Fromme Weisen, Angel Serenade

Anmerkung/Note:

Hum 718/A-E, 214/D/O Erste Ausgabe 1999.

First Issue 1999.

Hum 720
Parademarsch · On Parade

Modell-Nr. Model No.	Größe / Size cm / inch	Modellierdatum Sculpting Date	
720	12,5 / 5.00	1994	OE

Editionen mit Sonderbodenbild/ Editions with special backstamp:

Modell-Nr. Model No.	Ausgabejahr Year	Ausgabeland Country	
720		"US Navy, US Marines,	CE
		US Air Force, US Coast Guard,	
		US Army"	
		US-Militär, US Military	

Anmerkung/Note:

Erste Ausgabe 1998 mit Sonderbodenbild im ersten Produktionsjahr.

First Issue 1998 with special backstamp in the first year of production.

Hum 721
Gratulantentrio · Trio Of Wishes

Modell-Nr. Model No.	Größe / Size cm / inch	Modellierdatum Sculpting Date	
721	16 / 6.25	1995	CE

Trio Collection "Gratulantentrio" 1997

Auf 20.000 Stück weltweit limitiert und einzeln nummeriert.

Zweite Sonderausgabe innerhalb der Trio Collection.

Trio Collection "Trio Of Wishes" 1997

Worldwide limited and numbered edition of 20,000 pcs.

Second edition in a three part series.

OE: Offene Edition / Open Edition
CE: Produktion beendet / Closed Edition
TWD: Vorübergehend nicht mehr in Produktion / Temporarily withdrawn from production

Hum 722
Die kleine Besucherin · Little Visitor

Modell-Nr. Model No.	Größe / Size cm / inch	Modellierdatum Sculpting Date	
722	9,5 / 3.75	1995	OE

Anmerkung/Note:

Aufstellschild, Sonderanfertigung für das Informationszentrum der W.Goebel Porzellanfabrik in Rödental, Deutschland. Erste Ausgabe 1996.

Special Visitor's Plaque for the Information Center of W.Goebel in Rödental, Germany. First Issue 1996.

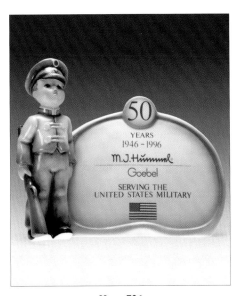

Hum 726
Stillgestanden! · Soldier Boy

Modell-Nr. Model No.	Größe / Size cm / inch	Modellierdatum Sculpting Date	
726	17 / 6.75	1995	TWD

50 Jahre Partnerschaft Goebel - US Militär 1996

Zur Feier dieses Jubiläums produzierte Goebel ein spezielles Aufstellschild, das exklusiv für das M.I.Hummel US-Militär Programm geschaffen wurde.
Auf 7.500 Stück weltweit limitiert und einzeln nummeriert.
Produktion beendet.

50 Years of Partnership Goebel - AAFES 1996

In celebration of this anniversary Goebel produced a special Jubilee Display Plaque exclusively created for the U.S. Military M.I.Hummel figurine program.
Worldwide limited and numbered edition of 7,500 pcs.
Closed Edition.

Hum 727
Muß noch umgraben · Garden Treasures

Modell-Nr. Model No.	Größe / Size cm / inch	Modellierdatum Sculpting Date	
727	9 / 3.50	1996	CE

Anmerkung/Note:

Exklusive Verlängerungsfigur für M.I.Hummel Clubmitglieder für das Clubjahr 1998/99.
Exclusive Renewal Figurine for members of the M.I.Hummel Club in the Club Years 1998/99.

OE: Offene Edition / Open Edition
CE: Produktion beendet / Closed Edition
TWD: Vorübergehend nicht mehr in Produktion / Temporarily withdrawn from production

Modell-Nr. Model No.	Größe / Size cm / inch	Modellierdatum Sculpting Date	
729	9 / 3.50	1995	CE

Hum 729
Muß noch gießen · Nature's Gift

Anmerkung/Note:

Exklusive Verlängerungsfigur für M.I.Hummel Clubmitglieder für das Clubjahr 1997/98.

Exclusive Renewal Figurine for members of the M.I.Hummel Club in the Club Years 1997/98.

Modell-Nr. Model No.	Größe / Size cm / inch	Modellierdatum Sculpting Date	
730	18,5 / 7.25	1978	CE

Hum 730
Mutters Liebste · Just Resting
Jubiläumsglocke · Anniversary Bell

Anmerkung/Note:

Kein Verkauf, nur Musterfertigung.

Never distributed, archives samples only.

Modell-Nr. Model No.	Größe / Size cm / inch	Modellierdatum Sculpting Date	
735	16 / 6.25	1985	CE

Hum 735
's ist kalt · It's Cold
Celebration Plate

Anmerkung/Note:

Exklusive Jahresedition für M.I.Hummel Clubmitglieder für das Clubjahr 1989/1990.

Exclusive Annual Edition for members of the M.I.Hummel Club in Club Year 1989/1990.

OE: Offene Edition / Open Edition
CE: Produktion beendet / Closed Edition
TWD: Vorübergehend nicht mehr in Produktion / Temporarily withdrawn from production

Modell-Nr. Model No.	Größe / Size cm / inch	Modellierdatum Sculpting Date	
736	16 / 6.25	1985	CE

Hum 736
Er liebt mich · Daisies Don't Tell
Celebration Plate

Anmerkung/Note:

Exklusive Jahresedition für M.I.Hummel Clubmitglieder für das Clubjahr 1988/1989.

Exclusive Annual Edition for members of the M.I.Hummel Club in Club Year 1988/1989.

Modell-Nr. Model No.	Größe / Size cm / inch	Modellierdatum Sculpting Date	
737	16 / 6.25	1985	CE

Hum 737
Herzjunge · Valentine Joy
Celebration Plate

Anmerkung/Note:

Exklusive Jahresedition für M.I.Hummel Clubmitglieder für das Clubjahr 1987/1988.

Exclusive Annual Edition for members of the M.I.Hummel Club in Club Year 1987/1988.

Modell-Nr. Model No.	Größe / Size cm / inch	Modellierdatum Sculpting Date	
738	16 / 6.25	1985	CE

Anmerkung/Note:

Exklusive Jahresedition für M.I.Hummel Clubmitglieder für das Clubjahr 1986/1987

Exclusive Annual Edition for members of the M.I.Hummel Club in Club Year 1986/1987.

Hum 738
I' hab' Di' gern · Valentine Gift
Celebration Plate

OE: Offene Edition / Open Edition
CE: Produktion beendet / Closed Edition
TWD: Vorübergehend nicht mehr in Produktion / Temporarily withdrawn from production

Modell-Nr. Model No.	Größe / Size cm / inch	Modellierdatum Sculpting Date	
739/I	15 / 6.00	1992	OE
739/II	20 / 8.00	1992	------------

Anmerkung/Note:

739/I Erste Ausgabe 1994 mit Sonderbodenbild im ersten Produktionsjahr; inklusive deutscher, europäischer und amerikanischer Fahne.

First Issue 1994 with special backstamp in the first year of production, including German, European and American flag.

739/II Noch nicht veröffentlicht, Possible Future Edition.

Hum 739
Fahnenträger · Call To Glory

Hum 741
Ständchen · Serenade

Hum 742
Herr Kapellmeister · Band Leader

Hum 743
Heldentenor · Soloist

Hum 744
Geigerlein · Little Fiddler

Hum 745
Kehrliesl · Little Sweeper

Hum 746
Große Wäsche · Wash Day

Hum 747
Zwei rechts - zwei links
A Stich In Time

Hum 748
Kükenliesl · Chicken - Licken

Modell-Nr. Model No.	Größe / Size cm / inch	Modellierdatum Sculpting Date		
Hum 741	10,5 / 4.25	1982	CE	Miniatur Sammlerteller 1985, Miniature Collector Plate 1985
Hum 742	10,5 / 4.25	1983	CE	Miniatur Sammlerteller 1987, Miniature Collector Plate 1987
Hum 743	10,5 / 4.25	1983	CE	Miniatur Sammlerteller 1986, Miniature Collector Plate 1986
Hum 744	10,5 / 4.25	1983	CE	Miniatur Sammlerteller 1984, Miniature Collector Plate 1984
Hum 745	10,5 / 4.25	1986	CE	Miniatur Sammlerteller 1988, Miniature Collector Plate 1988
Hum 746	10,5 / 4.25	1986	CE	Miniatur Sammlerteller 1989, Miniature Collector Plate 1989
Hum 747	10,5 / 4.25	1986	CE	Miniatur Sammlerteller 1990, Miniature Collector Plate 1990
Hum 748	10,5 / 4.25	1986	CE	Miniatur Sammlerteller 1991, Miniature Collector Plate 1991

Hum 750
Gänseliesl · Goose Girl
Jahresuhr · Anniversary Clock

Modell-Nr. Model No.	Größe / Size cm / inch	Modellierdatum Sculpting Date	
750	30 / 11.75	1993	TWD

Anmerkung/Note:

Erste Ausgabe 1995.

First Issue 1995.

OE: Offene Edition / Open Edition
CE: Produktion beendet / Closed Edition
TWD: Vorübergehend nicht mehr in Produktion / Temporarily withdrawn from production

Modell-Nr. Model No.	Größe / Size cm / inch	Modellierdatum Sculpting Date	
751	16,5 / 6.50	1993	CE

Hum 751
Hab' mein Wagen voll geladen
Love's Bounty

Anmerkung/Note:

Elfte Figur der "Century Collection" im Jahre 1996, deren Produktion auf ein Jahr im 20. Jahrhundert beschränkt war. Ein spezieller Sonderbodenstempel und ein Zertifikat bestätigten die Zugehörigkeit zur Serie.

Eleventh figurine in the "Century Collection" in 1996, which was produced for this one year only in the twentieth century. This was attested by a certifitate of authenticity and a special backstamp on the bottom of the figurine.

Modell-Nr. Model No.	Größe / Size cm / inch	Modellierdatum Sculpting Date	
754	9 / 3.50	1992	CE

Hum 754
Bringe uns den Frieden
We Come In Peace

UNICEF Sonderausgabe.
UNICEF Special Edition.

Modell-Nr. Model No.	Größe / Size cm / inch	Modellierdatum Sculpting Date	
755/0	9,5 / 3.75	1999	TWD
755	20 / 8.00	1992	TWD

Anmerkung/Note:

755 Erste Ausgabe 1994 mit Sonderbodenbild im ersten Produktionsjahr.

    First Issue 1994 with special backstamp in the first year of production.

Christbaumspitze und Figur, Christmas Tree Topper and Figurine.

755/0 Sonderanfertigung 1999 für USA.

    Special Edition 1999 for the US.

Hum 755
Christkindlein kommt · Heavenly Angel

OE: Offene Edition / Open Edition
CE: Produktion beendet / Closed Edition
TWD: Vorübergehend nicht mehr in Produktion / Temporarily withdrawn from production

Hum 756
Kunstmaler · The Artist

Modell-Nr. Model No.	Größe / Size cm / inch	Modellierdatum Sculpting Date	
756	12 / 4.75	1993	TWD

Editionen mit Sonderbodenbild/ Editions with special backstamp:

Modell-Nr. Model No.	Ausgabejahr Year	Ausgabeland Country	
756	1993	"New Braunfels" USA	CE
756	1994	"New Braunfels" USA	CE
756	1994	"Kevelaer" Deutschland, Germany	CE
756	1994	"Kitzingen" Deutschland, Germany	CE
756	1996	"New Braunfels" USA	CE
756	1997	"20th Anniversary Eaton" USA	CE
756	1997	"Berta Hummel Museum" Deutschland, Germany	CE

Hum 757
Unter der Laterne · A Tuneful Trio

Modell-Nr. Model No.	Größe / Size cm / inch	Modellierdatum Sculpting Date	
757	17 / 6.75	1993	CE

Trio Collection "Unter der Laterne" 1996

Auf 20.000 Stück weltweit limitiert und einzeln nummeriert.

Erste Sonderausgabe innerhalb der Trio Collection.

Trio Collection "A Tuneful Trio" 1996

Worldwide limited and numbered edition of 20,000 pcs.

First edition in a three part series.

Hum 758
Für Mutti · Nimble Fingers

Modell-Nr. Model No.	Größe / Size cm / inch	Modellierdatum Sculpting Date	
758	13 / 5.25	1993	OE

Anmerkung/Note:

Erste Ausgabe 1996 mit Sonderbodenbild im ersten Produktionsjahr.

First Issue 1996 with special backstamp in the first year of production.

Mit Holzbank, Wooden bench included.

OE: Offene Edition / Open Edition
CE: Produktion beendet / Closed Edition
TWD: Vorübergehend nicht mehr in Produktion / Temporarily withdrawn from production

Modell-Nr. Model No.	Größe / Size cm / inch	Modellierdatum Sculpting Date	
759	13 / 5.25	1993	OE

Anmerkung/Note:

Erste Ausgabe 1995 mit Sonderbodenbild im ersten Produktionsjahr.

First Issue 1995 with special backstamp in the first year of production.

Mit Holzstuhl, Wooden chair included.

Hum 759
Für Vati · To Keep You Warm

Modell-Nr. Model No.	Größe / Size cm / inch	Modellierdatum Sculpting Date	
760	14 / 5.50	1993	CE

Anmerkung/Note:

Exklusive Jahresedition für M.I.Hummel Clubmitglieder für das Clubjahr 1995/1996.

Exclusive Annual Edition for members of the M.I.Hummel Club in Club Year 1995/1996.

Hum 760
In die weite Welt · Country Suitor

Modell-Nr. Model No.	Größe / Size cm / inch	Modellierdatum Sculpting Date	
761	9 / 3.50	1993	OE

Editionen mit Sonderbodenbild/ Editions with special backstamp:

Modell-Nr. Model No.	Ausgabejahr Year	Ausgabeland Country	
761	1998	"Brinkmann" Deutschland, Germany	CE
761	2000	Weltausstellung Hannover	CE

Anmerkung/Note:

Erste Ausgabe 1996 mit Sonderbodenbild im ersten Produktionsjahr.

First Issue 1996 with special backstamp in the first year of production.

Hum 761
Für Dich · From The Heart

OE: Offene Edition / Open Edition
CE: Produktion beendet / Closed Edition
TWD: Vorübergehend nicht mehr in Produktion / Temporarily withdrawn from production

Modell-Nr. Model No.	Größe / Size cm / inch	Modellierdatum Sculpting Date	
762	9 / 3.50	1993	OE

Hum 762
Ein Röschen für Dich · Roses Are Red

Anmerkung/Note:

Erste Ausgabe 1998 mit Sonderbodenbild im ersten Produktionsjahr.

First Issue 1998 with special backstamp in the first year of production.

Modell-Nr. Model No.	Größe / Size cm / inch	Modellierdatum Sculpting Date	
766	27 / 10.75	1994	CE

Hum 766
Ein Herz für Dich · Here's My Heart

Anmerkung/Note:

Dreizehnte Figur der "Century Collection" im Jahre 1998, deren Produktion auf ein Jahr im 20. Jahrhundert beschränkt war. Ein spezieller Sonderbodenstempel und ein Zertifikat bestätigten die Zugehörigkeit zur Serie.

Thirteenth figurine in the "Century Collection" in 1998, which was produced for this one year only in the twentieth century. This was attested by a certificate of authenticity and a special backstamp on the bottom of the figurine.

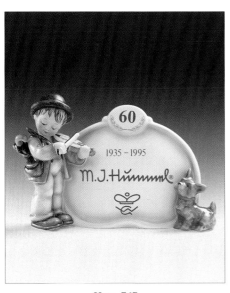

Modell-Nr. Model No.	Größe / Size cm / inch	Modellierdatum Sculpting Date	
767	19 / 7.50	1993	CE

Hum 767
Geigerlein mit Hund · Puppy Love

Sonderausgabe 1995

Aufstellschild, Sonderausgabe 60 Jahre M.I. Hummel Figuren.

Produktion beendet.

Special Edition 1995

Display Plaque.

Closed Edition.

OE: Offene Edition / Open Edition
CE: Produktion beendet / Closed Edition
TWD: Vorübergehend nicht mehr in Produktion / Temporarily withdrawn from production

Modell-Nr. Model No.	Größe / Size cm / inch	Modellierdatum Sculpting Date	
768	9 / 3.50	1993	OE

Editionen mit Sonderbodenbild/ Editions with special backstamp:

Modell-Nr. Model No.	Ausgabejahr Year	Ausgabeland Country	
768	1998	"Budapest" Ungarn, Hungary	CE

Anmerkung/Note:

Erste Ausgabe 1995 mit Sonderbodenbild im ersten Produktionsjahr.

First Issue 1995 with special backstamp in the first year of production.

Hum 768
Süßer Fratz · Pixie

Modell-Nr. Model No.	Größe / Size cm / inch	Modellierdatum Sculpting Date	
771	12 / 4.75	1994	OE

Anmerkung/Note:

Erste Ausgabe 1997 mit Sonderbodenbild im ersten Produktionsjahr.

First Issue 1997 with special backstamp in the first year of production.

Mit Schaukelstuhl, Wooden rocking chair included.

Hum 771
Übungsstunde · Practice Makes Perfekt

Hum 775
Fahrt in die Weihnacht
Ride Into Christmas

Hum 776
Brief ans Christkind
Letter To Santa Claus

Hum 777
Hört Ihr Leute · Hear Ye, Hear Ye

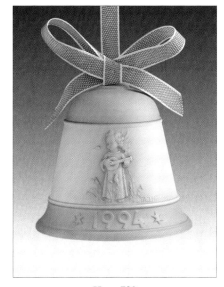

Hum 778
Sängerquartett
Harmony In Four Parts

Hum 779
Himmlische Klänge · Celestial Musician

Hum 780
Adventsengel mit Mandoline
Festival Harmony (Mandolin)

Hum 781
Adventsengel mit Flöte
Festival Harmony (Flute)

Hum 782
Weihnachtslied · Christmas Song

Hum 783
Dankgebet · Thanksgiving Prayer

Hum 784
Leise Töne · Echoes Of Joy

Hum 785
Festliche Trompetenklänge
A Joyful Noise

Hum 786
Ich leuchte Dir den Weg
Light The Way

Modell-Nr. Model No.	Größe / Size cm / inch	Modellierdatum Sculpting Date	
793	10 / 4.00	1994	CE

Anmerkung/Note:

Exklusive Verlängerungsfigur für M.I.Hummel Clubmitglieder für das Clubjahr 1996/97.

Exclusive Renewal Figurine for members of the M.I.Hummel Club in Club Year 1996/97.

Hum 793
Herzlich Willkommen · Forever Yours

Modell-Nr. Model No.	Größe / Size cm / inch	Modellierdatum Sculpting Date	
795/0	12 / 4.75	1994	OE
795/I	14 / 5.50	1996	-------------

Editionen mit Sonderbodenbild/ Editions with special backstamp:

Modell-Nr. Model No.	Ausgabejahr Year	Ausgabeort Country	
795/0	1997	"Luzern" Schweiz, Switzerland	CE

Anmerkung/Note:

795/0 Erste Ausgabe 1997 mit Sonderbodenbild im ersten Produktionsjahr.

First Issue 1997 with special backstamp in the first year of production.

795/I Noch nicht veröffentlicht. Possible Future Edition.

Hum 795
Aus meinem Garten · From My Garden

Modell-Nr. Model No.	Größe / Size cm / inch	Modellierdatum Sculpting Date	
800	9 / 3.50	1996	OE

Editionen mit Sonderbodenbild/ Editions with special backstamp:

Modell-Nr. Model No.	Ausgabejahr Year	Ausgabeland Country	
800	1999	USA	CE
800	2000	Karibik, Caribbean	CE
800	2000	"St. Thomas" Karibik, Caribbean	CE

Anmerkung/Note:

Erste Ausgabe 2000 mit Sonderbodenbild im ersten Produktionsjahr.

First Issue 2000 with special backstamp in the first year of production.

OE:	Offene Edition / Open Edition
CE:	Produktion beendet / Closed Edition
TWD:	Vorübergehend nicht mehr in Produktion / Temporarily withdrawn from production

Hum 800
Hörst Du zu? · Proud Moments

Hum 806
Bulgarischer Flötenspieler
Bulgarian

Hum 807
Bulgarisches Mädchen
Bulgarian

Hum 808
Bulgarischer Dudelsackspieler
Bulgarian

Hum 809
Bulgarisches Mädchen mit Hühnern
Bulgarian

Hum 810
Bulgarisches tanzendes Mädchen
Bulgarian

Hum 810
Bulgarisches tanzendes Mädchen
Bulgarian

Hum 811
Bulgarischer tanzender Junge
Bulgarian

Hum 812
Bulgarisches Mädchen
Bulgarian

Hum 812
Bulgarisches Mädchen
Bulgarian

Modell-Nr. Model No.	Größe / Size cm / inch	Modellierdatum Sculpting Date	
Hum 824	12 / 4.75	1940	CE
Hum 825	13,5 / 5.50	1940	CE

Hum 825
Schwedisches Mädchen
Swedish

Anmerkung/Note:

Vom Kloster Sießen nicht genehmigt. Kein Verkauf, nur Musterfertigung.

Not approved by the Convent of Siessen. Never distributed, archives samples only.

Modell-Nr. Model No.	Größe / Size cm / inch	Modellierdatum Sculpting Date	
826/2/0	9 / 3.50	1997	-------------
826/I	13,5 / 5.25	1997	OE

Hum 826
Der große Maestro · Little Maestro

Anmerkung/Note:

826/2/0 Noch nicht veröffentlicht. Possible Future Edition.

Sammler Set "Der große Maestro" 2000

bestehend aus Hum 826/I und Teddybär der Firma Steiff.

Der Teddybär ist auf 20.000 Stück weltweit limitiert und einzeln nummeriert.

Erste Ausgabe 2000 mit Sonderbodenbild im ersten Produktionsjahr.

Collector's Set "Little Meastro" 2000

consisting of Hum 826/I and Steiff Teddybaer.

The Teddy is a worldwide limited and numbered edition of 20,000 pcs.

First Issue 2000 with special backstamp in the first year of production.

Sammler Set "Der große Maestro"
Collectors Set "Little Maestro"

OE: Offene Edition / Open Edition
CE: Produktion beendet / Closed Edition
TWD: Vorübergehend nicht mehr in Produktion / Temporarily withdrawn from production

Hum 806
Bulgarischer Flötenspieler
Bulgarian

Hum 807
Bulgarisches Mädchen
Bulgarian

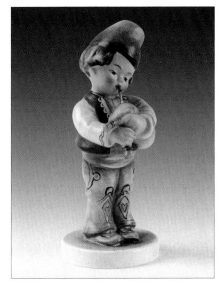

Hum 808
Bulgarischer Dudelsackspieler
Bulgarian

Hum 809
Bulgarisches Mädchen mit Hühnern
Bulgarian

Hum 810
Bulgarisches tanzendes Mädchen
Bulgarian

Hum 810
Bulgarisches tanzendes Mädchen
Bulgarian

Hum 811
Bulgarischer tanzender Junge
Bulgarian

Hum 812
Bulgarisches Mädchen
Bulgarian

Hum 812
Bulgarisches Mädchen
Bulgarian

Modell-Nr. Model No.	Größe / Size cm / inch	Modellierdatum Sculpting Date	
Hum 806	12 / 4.75	1940	CE
Hum 807	12,5 / 5.00	1940	CE
Hum 808	12 / 4.75	1940	CE
Hum 809	12,5 / 5.00	1940	CE
Hum 810	12,5 / 5.00	1940	CE
Hum 811	13 / 5.25	1940	CE
Hum 812	13 / 5.25	1940	CE
Hum 813	13 / 5.25	1940	CE
Hum 814	13 / 5.25	1940	CE

Hum 813
Serbischer Junge
Serbian

Anmerkung/Note:

Vom Kloster Sießen nicht genehmigt. Kein Verkauf, nur Musterfertigung.

Not approved by the Convent of Siessen. Never distributed, archives samples only.

Modell-Nr. Model No.	Größe / Size cm / inch	Modellierdatum Sculpting Date	
814	12 / 4.75	1996	OE

Hum 814
Erstkommunion (Mädchen)
Peaceful Blessing

Anmerkung/Note:

Erste Ausgabe 1999 mit Sonderbodenbild im ersten Produktionsjahr.

First Issue 1999 with special backstamp in the first year of production.

Modell-Nr. Model No.	Größe / Size cm / inch	Modellierdatum Sculpting Date	
815	12,5 / 5.00	1996	OE

Anmerkung/Note:

Erste Ausgabe 1999 mit Sonderbodenbild im ersten Produktionsjahr.

First Issue 1999 with special backstamp in the first year of production.

OE: Offene Edition / Open Edition
CE: Produktion beendet / Closed Edition
TWD: Vorübergehend nicht mehr in Produktion / Temporarily withdrawn from production

Hum 815
Erstkommunion (Junge) · Heavenly Prayer

Modell-Nr. Model No.	Größe / Size cm / inch	Modellierdatum Sculpting Date	
820	9 / 3.50	1997	TWD

Hum 820
Ade · Adieu
Aufstellschild · Plaque

Editionen mit Sonderbodenbild/ Editions with special backstamp:

Modell-Nr. Model No.	Ausgabejahr Year	Ausgabeland Country	
820	1999	Karibik, Caribbean	CE
820	1999	Karibik, Caribbean	CE

Modell-Nr. Model No.	Größe / Size cm / inch	Modellierdatum Sculpting Date	
822	11 / 4.25	1997	OE

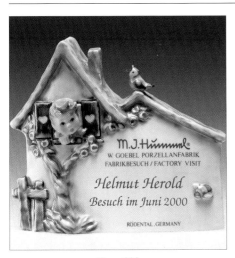

Hum 822
Hummelnest · Hummelnest

Anmerkung/Note:

Aufstellschild, Sonderanfertigung für das Informationszentrum der W.Goebel Porzellanfabrik in Rödental, Deutschland. Erste Ausgabe 1997.

Special Visitor's Plaque for the Information Center of W.Goebel in Rödental, Germany. First Issue 1997.

Keine Archivmuster vorhanden.
No Samples available in our Archives.

Hum 824 Schwedischer Junge Swedish	**Hum 824** Schwedischer Junge Swedish	**Hum 825** Schwedisches Mädchen Swedish

Modell-Nr. Model No.	Größe / Size cm / inch	Modellierdatum Sculpting Date	
Hum 824	12 / 4.75	1940	CE
Hum 825	13,5 / 5.50	1940	CE

**Hum 825
Schwedisches Mädchen
Swedish**

Anmerkung/Note:

Vom Kloster Sießen nicht genehmigt. Kein Verkauf, nur Musterfertigung.

Not approved by the Convent of Siessen. Never distributed, archives samples only.

Modell-Nr. Model No.	Größe / Size cm / inch	Modellierdatum Sculpting Date	
826/2/0	9 / 3.50	1997	-------------
826/I	13,5 / 5.25	1997	OE

**Hum 826
Der große Maestro · Little Maestro**

Anmerkung/Note:

826/2/0 Noch nicht veröffentlicht. Possible Future Edition.

Sammler Set "Der große Maestro" 2000

bestehend aus Hum 826/I und Teddybär der Firma Steiff.

Der Teddybär ist auf 20.000 Stück weltweit limitiert und einzeln nummeriert.

Erste Ausgabe 2000 mit Sonderbodenbild im ersten Produktionsjahr.

Collector's Set "Little Meastro" 2000

consisting of Hum 826/I and Steiff Teddybaer.

The Teddy is a worldwide limited and numbered edition of 20,000 pcs.

First Issue 2000 with special backstamp in the first year of production.

**Sammler Set "Der große Maestro"
Collectors Set "Little Maestro"**

OE: Offene Edition / Open Edition
CE: Produktion beendet / Closed Edition
TWD: Vorübergehend nicht mehr in Produktion / Temporarily withdrawn from production

Hum 827
Ein Küßchen als Gruß · Daydreamer

Modell-Nr. Model No.	Größe / Size cm / inch	Modellierdatum Sculpting Date	
827	9 / 3.50	1998	OE

Anmerkung/Note:

Nur erhältlich während einer Malvorführung.

Only available during Artist Promotions.

Hum 828
Meinst mich? · Over The Horizon

Modell-Nr. Model No.	Größe / Size cm / inch	Modellierdatum Sculpting Date	
828	8,5 / 3.25	1998	OE

Anmerkung/Note:

Nur erhältlich während einer Malvorführung.

Only available during Artist Promotions.

Hum 829
Wo geht's hin? · Glow Of Freedom

Modell-Nr. Model No.	Größe / Size cm / inch	Modellierdatum Sculpting Date	
829	16,5 / 6.50	1999	OE

Anmerkung/Note:

Sonderausgabe "Enduring Glow Of Freedom" nur für US Truppen 1999.

Bestehend aus Hum 829 und Hum 109.

Auf 5.000 Stück weltweit limitiert und einzeln numeriert.

Special Edition "Enduring Glow Of Freedom" for U.S. Military 1999.

Consisting of Hum 829 and Hum 109.

Worldwide limited and numbered edition of 5,000 pcs.

OE: Offene Edition / Open Edition
CE: Produktion beendet / Closed Edition
TWD: Vorübergehend nicht mehr in Produktion / Temporarily withdrawn from production

Hum 831
Slowakischer Junge mit Flöte
Slovak

Hum 832
Slowakisches Mädchen
Slovak

Hum 832
Slowakisches Mädchen
Slovak

Modell-Nr. Model No.	Größe / Size cm / inch	Modellierdatum Sculpting Date	
Hum 831	14 / 5.75	1940	CE
Hum 832	14,5 / 5.75	1940	CE
Hum 833	14 / 5.75	1940	CE
Hum 834	14 / 5.75	1940	CE

Anmerkung/Note:

Kein Verkauf, nur Musterfertigung.

Never distributed, archives samples only.

Hum 833
Slowakischer Junge mit Dudelsack
Slovak

Hum 834
Slowakischer Junge mit Geige
Slovak

Modell-Nr. Model No.	Größe / Size cm / inch	Modellierdatum Sculpting Date	
835	8 / 3.25	1998	OE

Anmerkung/Note:

Erste Ausgabe 2000 mit Sonderbodenbild im ersten Produktionsjahr.

First Issue 2000 with special backstamp in the first year of production.

Hum 835
Maiglöckchen · Garden Splendor

OE: Offene Edition / Open Edition
CE: Produktion beendet / Closed Edition
TWD: Vorübergehend nicht mehr in Produktion / Temporarily withdrawn from production

Modell-Nr. Model No.	Größe / Size cm / inch	Modellierdatum Sculpting Date	
836	9 / 3.50	1999	OE

Hum 836
Der kleine Träumer · Afternoon Nap

Anmerkung/Note:

Erste Ausgabe 2001 mit Sonderbodenbild im ersten Produktionsjahr.

First Issue 2001 with special backstamp in the first year of production.

Hum 841
Tschechischer Junge mit Lamm
Czech

Hum 842
Tschechisches Mädchen
Czech

Hum 842
Tschechisches Mädchen
Czech

Hum 851
Ungarischer Junge
Hungarian

Hum 851
Ungarischer Junge
Hungarian

Hum 852
Ungarisches tanzendes Mädchen
Hungarian

Hum 852
Ungarisches tanzendes Mädchen
Hungarian

Hum 853
Ungarischer Junge mit Blumen
Hungarian

Hum 853
Ungarischer Junge mit Blumen
Hungarian

Hum 854
Ungarisches Mädchen
Hungarian

Modell-Nr. Model No.	Größe / Size cm / inch	Modellierdatum Sculpting Date	
Hum 841	14 / 5.75	1940	CE
Hum 842	14 / 5.75	1940	CE
Hum 851	13 / 5.25	1940	CE
Hum 852	12,5 / 5.00	1940	CE
Hum 853	13,5 / 5.50	1940	CE
Hum 854	13 / 5.25	1940	CE

Anmerkung/Note:

Kein Verkauf, nur Musterfertigung.

Never distributed, archives samples only.

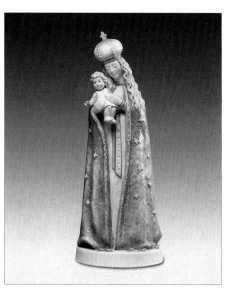

Hum 855
Millennium Madonna

Modell-Nr. Model No.	Größe / Size cm / inch	Modellierdatum Sculpting Date	
855	26 /10.25	2000	CE

Sonderausgabe "Millennium Madonna" 2000
Auf 7.500 Stück weltweit limitiert und einzeln numeriert.
Produktion beendet.

Special Edition "Millennium Madonna" 2000
Worldwide limited and numbered edition of 7,500 pcs.
Closed Edition.

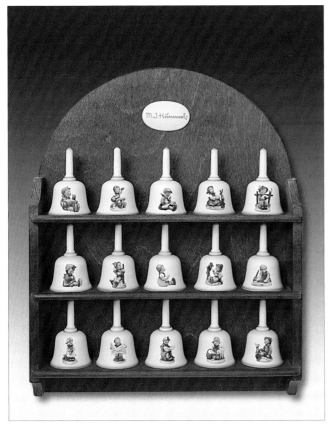

Holzregal "rustikal"
Wooden Board "countrystyle"

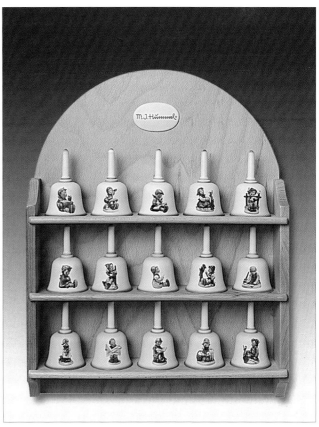

Holzregal "hell"
Wooden Board "light brown"

Modell-Nr. Model No.	Größe / Size cm / inch	Modellierdatum Sculpting Date		
860	9,5 / 3.75	1999	OE seit / since 2000	Heini, Bandoneonspieler, Let's Sing
861	9,5 / 3.75	1999	OE seit / since 2000	Auf Wiedersehen, Farewell
862	9,5 / 3.75	1999	OE seit / since 2000	Der Gelehrte, Thoughtful
863	9,5 / 3.75	1999	OE seit / since 2000	Mach's nach, In Tune
864	9,5 / 3.75	1999	OE seit / since 2000	Liebt mich, liebt mich nicht..., She Loves Me, She Loves Me Not...
865	9,5 / 3.75	1999	OE seit / since 2000	Der erste Strumpf, Knit One, Purl One
866	9,5 / 3.75	1999	OE seit / since 2000	I' hab's erreicht, Mountaineer
867	9,5 / 3.75	1999	OE seit / since 2000	Die kleine Sängerin, Girl With Sheet Music
868	9,5 / 3.75	1999	OE seit / since 2000	Auf los geht's los, Sing Along
869	9,5 / 3.75	1999	OE seit / since 2000	Ein dicker Gruß, With Loving Greetings
870	9,5 / 3.75	1999	OE ab / in 2001	Musterschülerin, Busy Student
871	9,5 / 3.75	1999	OE ab / in 2001	Das Allerneueste, Latest News
872	9,5 / 3.75	1999	OE ab / in 2001	Was gibt's Neues?, What's New?
873	9,5 / 3.75	1999	OE ab / in 2001	Osterüberraschung, Favorite Pet
874	9,5 / 3.75	1999	OE ab / in 2001	Ein frohes Lied, Whistler's Duet

Anmerkung/Note:

Miniatur - Jahresglocken - Reproduktionen.

Miniature Bells (Reproductions of the Annual Bells).

Hum 876/A
Christkindlein kommt · Heavenly Angel

Modell-Nr. Model No.	Größe / Size cm / inch	Modellierdatum Sculpting Date	
876/A	8,5 / 3.25	1999	OE

Anmerkung/Note:

Christbaumschmuck Glocke. Erste Ausgabe 1999.

Christmas Tree Ornament Bell. First Issue 1999.

Hum 877/A
Fahrt in die Weihnacht
Ride Into Christmas

Modell-Nr. Model No.	Größe / Size cm / inch	Modellierdatum Sculpting Date	
877/A	10,5 / 4.25	1999	OE

Anmerkung/Note:

Christbaumschmuck Weihnachtsbaum. Erste Ausgabe 1999.

Christmas Tree Ornament Christmas Tree. First Issue 1999.

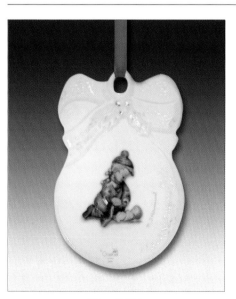

Hum 878/A
Schlaf gut · Sleep Tight

Modell-Nr. Model No.	Größe / Size cm / inch	Modellierdatum Sculpting Date	
878/A	9 / 3.50	1999	OE

Anmerkung/Note:

Christbaumschmuck Kugel. Erste Ausgabe 1999.

Christmas Tree Ornament Ball. First Issue 1999.

OE: Offene Edition / Open Edition
CE: Produktion beendet / Closed Edition
TWD: Vorübergehend nicht mehr in Produktion / Temporarily withdrawn from production

Holzregal "rustikal"
Wooden Board "countrystyle"

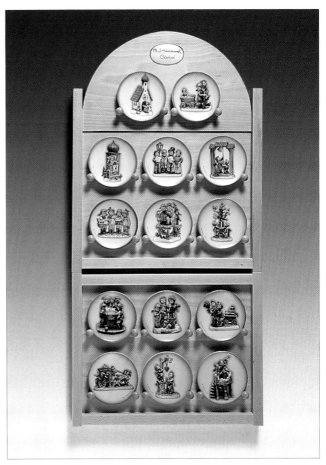

Holzregal "hell"
Wooden Board "light brown"

Modell-Nr. Model No.	Größe / Size cm / inch	Modellierdatum Sculpting Date		
886	10 / 4.00	1997	OE seit / since 1999	Bergkirchlein, Chapel Time
887	10 / 4.00	1997	OE seit / since 1999	Frohe Fahrt, Pleasant Journey
888	10 / 4.00	1997	OE seit / since 1999	Glockenturm, Call To Worship
889	10 / 4.00	1997	OE seit / since 1999	Sängerquartett, Harmony In Four Parts
890	10 / 4.00	1997	OE seit / since 1999	Sturmläuten, Let's Tell The World
891	10 / 4.00	1997	OE seit / since 1999	Wir wünschen Dir das Beste, We Wish You The Best
892	10 / 4.00	1997	OE seit / since 1999	Bald sind wir drüben, On Our Way
893	10 / 4.00	1997	OE seit / since 1999	Frühlingstanz, Welcome Spring
894	10 / 4.00	1997	OE seit / since 1999	Das Nesthäckchen, Rock-A-Bye
895	10 / 4.00	1997	OE seit / since 1999	Viel Glück, Strike Up The Band
896	10 / 4.00	1997	OE seit / since 1999	Hab' mein Wagen voll geladen, Love's Bounty
897	10 / 4.00	1997	OE seit / since 1999	Es wär' so schön gewesen, Fond Good-Bye
898	10 / 4.00	1997	OE seit / since 1999	Ein Herz für Dich, Here's My Heart
899	10 / 4.00	1997	OE seit / since 1999	Turmbläser, Fanfare

Anmerkung/Note:

Century Collection Teller.

Century Collection Plates.

Hum 900
Wanderbub · Merry Wanderer

Modell-Nr. Model No.	Größe / Size cm / inch	Modellierdatum Sculpting Date	
900	10,5 / 4.25	1997	Nur für authorisierte Fachhändler
			Only available for authorized dealers
900	10,5 / 4.25	1997	CE, M.I.Hummel Club

Anmerkung/Note:

Das Händler Aufstellschild wird in neun Sprachversionen produziert, Deutsch, Englisch, Amerikanisch, Holländisch, Italienisch, Französisch, Schwedisch, Spanisch und Japanisch.

This Retailer plaque was issued in nine decal variations for use in other languages, German, British, US, Dutch, Italian, French, Swedish, Spanish and Japanese version.

Hum 900
Wanderbub · Merry Wanderer
Club Sonderedition · Club Special Edition

Sonderedition des M.I.Hummel Club

Exklusive Sonderedition für M.I.Hummel Clubmitglieder für das Clubjahr 1999/2000. Produktion beendet.

Special Edition of the M.I.Hummel Club

Exclusive Special Edition for members of the M.I.Hummel Club in Club Year 1999/2000. Closed Edition.

Hum 904
Serbischer Junge · Serbian

Modell-Nr. Model No.	Größe / Size cm / inch	Modellierdatum Sculpting Date	
904	13 / 5.2.5	1940	CE

Anmerkung/Note:

Kein Verkauf, nur Musterfertigung.

Never distributed, archives samples only.

OE: Offene Edition / Open Edition
CE: Produktion beendet / Closed Edition
TWD: Vorübergehend nicht mehr in Produktion / Temporarily withdrawn from production

Hum 913
Serbisches Mädchen · Serbian

Modell-Nr. Model No.	Größe / Size cm / inch	Modellierdatum Sculpting Date	
913	12 / 4.75	1940	CE

Anmerkung/Note:

Kein Verkauf, nur Musterfertigung.

Never distributed, archives samples only.

Hum 920
Sterngucker · Star Gazer

Modell-Nr. Model No.	Größe / Size cm / inch	Modellierdatum Sculpting Date	
920	19 / 7.50	1999	CE

Anmerkung/Note:

Millennium Teller 2000, nur für USA.

Millennium Plate 2000, for the US only.

Hum 921
Maiglöckchen · Garden Splendor

Modell-Nr. Model No.	Größe / Size cm / inch	Modellierdatum Sculpting Date	
921	18 / 7.00	1999	CE

Anmerkung/Note:

Jahresteller 2000.

Annual Plate 2000.

OE: Offene Edition / Open Edition
CE: Produktion beendet / Closed Edition
TWD: Vorübergehend nicht mehr in Produktion / Temporarily withdrawn from production

Modell-Nr. Model No.	Größe / Size cm / inch	Modellierdatum Sculpting Date	
922	18 / 7.00	1999	OE

Hum 922
Der kleine Träumer · Afternoon Nap

Anmerkung/Note:

Jahresteller 2001.

Annual Plate 2001.

Modell-Nr. Model No.	Größe / Size cm / inch	Modellierdatum Sculpting Date	
947	12,5 / 5.00	1940	CE

Hum 947
Serbisches Mädchen · Serbian

Anmerkung/Note:

Vom Kloster Sießen nicht genehmigt. Kein Verkauf, nur Musterfertigung.

Not approved by the Convent of Siessen. Never distributed, archives samples only.

Modell-Nr. Model No.	Größe / Size cm / inch	Modellierdatum Sculpting Date	
968	14 / 5.75	1940	CE

Hum 968
Serbischer Junge · Serbian

Anmerkung/Note:

Kein Verkauf, nur Musterfertigung.

Never distributed, archives samples only.

OE: Offene Edition / Open Edition
CE: Produktion beendet / Closed Edition
TWD: Vorübergehend nicht mehr in Produktion / Temporarily withdrawn from production

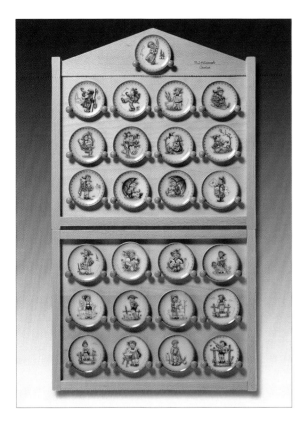

Miniatur - Jahresteller - Reproduktionen.

Mini Plates (Reproductions of the Annual Plates).

Originalgröße   original size

Modell-Nr. Model No.	Größe / Size cm / inch	Modellierdatum Sculpting Date		
971	8 / 3.25	1996	OE seit / since 1997	Christkindlein kommt, Heavenly Angel
972	8 / 3.25	1996	OE seit / since 1997	Hört' Ihr Leute, Hear Ye, Hear Ye
973	8 / 3.25	1996	OE seit / since 1997	Hinaus in die Ferne, Happy Traveller
974	8 / 3.25	1996	OE seit / since 1997	Gänseliesl, Goose Girl
975	8 / 3.25	1996	OE seit / since 1997	Fahrt in die Weihnacht, Ride Into Christmas
976	8 / 3.25	1996	OE seit / since 1997	Frühling, Apple Tree Girl
977	8 / 3.25	1996	OE seit / since 1997	Herbst, Apple Tree Boy
978	8 / 3.25	1996	OE seit / since 1997	Strickliesl, Happy Pastime
979	8 / 3.25	1996	OE seit / since 1997	's stimmt net, Singing Lesson
980	8 / 3.25	1996	OE seit / since 1997	Erster Schulgang, School Girl
981	8 / 3.25	1996	OE seit / since 1997	Geborgen Junge, Umbrella Boy
982	8 / 3.25	1996	OE seit / since 1997	Geborgen Mädchen, Umbrella Girl
983	8 / 3.25	1996	OE seit / since 1998	Eilbote, Postman
984	8 / 3.25	1996	OE seit / since 1998	Fleißiges Lieschen, Little Helper
985	8 / 3.25	1996	OE seit / since 1998	Kükenmütterchen, Chick Girl
986	8 / 3.25	1996	OE seit / since 1998	Hasenvater, Playmates
987	8 / 3.25	1997	OE seit / since 1998	Im Hühnerhof, Feeding Time
988	8 / 3.25	1997	OE seit / since 1998	Ziegenbub, Little Goat Herder
989	8 / 3.25	1997	OE seit / since 1998	Schweinehirt, Farm Boy
990	8 / 3.25	1997	OE seit / since 1998	Schäferbub, Shepherd's Boy
991	8 / 3.25	1997	OE seit / since 1998	Mutters Liebste, Just Resting
992	8 / 3.25	1997	OE seit / since 1998	Vaters G'scheitester, Wayside Harmony
993	8 / 3.25	1997	OE seit / since 1998	Puppenbad, Doll Bath
994	8 / 3.25	1997	OE seit / since 1998	Puppendoktor, Doctor
995	8 / 3.25	1997	OE seit / since 1998	Bleib nicht so lange fort, Come Back Soon

Modell-Nr. Model No.	Größe / Size cm / inch	Modellierdatum Sculpting Date	
1999	28 / 11.00	1997	CE

Anmerkung/Note:

Vierzehnte und letzte Figur der "Century Collection" im Jahre 1999, deren Produktion auf ein Jahr im 20. Jahrhundert beschränkt war. Ein spezieller Sonderbodenstempel und ein Zertifikat bestätigten die Zugehörigkeit zur Serie.

Fourteenth and final figurine in the "Century Collection" in 1999, which was produced for this one year only in the twentieth century. This was attested by a certifitate of authenticity and a special backstamp on the bottom of the figurines.

Hum 1999
Turmbläser · Fanfare

Modell-Nr. Model No.	Größe / Size cm / inch	Modellierdatum Sculpting Date	
2000	20 / 8.00	1998	CE

Limitierte Ausgabe "Gemeinsam um die Welt" 2000

Auf 2.000 Stück weltweit limitiert und einzeln nummeriert.
Produktion beendet.

Limited Edition "Worldwide Wanderers" 2000

Worldwide limited and numbered edition of 2,000 pcs.
Closed Edition.

Hum 2000
Gemeinsam um die Welt
Worldwide Wanderers

Modell-Nr. Model No.	Größe / Size cm / inch	Modellierdatum Sculpting Date	
2002	16,5 / 6.50	1996	OE

Anmerkung/Note:

Erste Ausgabe 1996 mit Sonderbodenbild im ersten Produktionsjahr.

First Issue 1996 with special backstamp in the first year of production.

Hum 2002
Winterfreunde · Making New Friends

OE: Offene Edition / Open Edition
CE: Produktion beendet / Closed Edition
TWD: Vorübergehend nicht mehr in Produktion / Temporarily withdrawn from production

Modell-Nr. Model No.	Größe / Size cm / inch	Modellierdatum Sculpting Date	
2003	17 / 6.75	1996	OE

Anmerkung/Note:

Erste Ausgabe 1998 mit Sonderbodenbild im ersten Produktionsjahr.

First Issue 1998 with special backstamp in the first year of production.

Ein neutrales Messingschild wird mitgeliefert. Es kann von einem Spezialisten anlaßbezogen graviert werden!

A neutral brass plaque is included. It can be engraved individually by a specialist!

Hum 2003
Hochzeit · Dearly Beloved

Modell-Nr. Model No.	Größe / Size cm / inch	Modellierdatum Sculpting Date	
2004	10,5 / 4.25	1996	OE

Editionen mit Sonderbodenbild/ Editions with special backstamp:

Modell-Nr. Model No.	Ausgabejahr Year	Ausgabeland Country	
2004	1999	"Grüße aus Amberg" Deutschland, Germany	CE
2004	1999	Deutschland, Germany	CE
2004	1999	"Two flags" USA	CE
2004	2000	"M.I.Hummel Club Convention" Deutschland, Germany	CE

Anmerkung/Note:

Erste Ausgabe 1999 mit Sonderbodenbild im ersten Produktionsjahr.

First Issue 1999 with special backstamp in the first year of production.

Hum 2004
Frisch gebacken · Pretzel Girl

Modell-Nr. Model No.	Größe / Size cm / inch	Modellierdatum Sculpting Date	
2007	11 / 4.25	1996	CE

Limitierte Ausgabe "Katzenmama" 1998

Auf 25.000 Stück weltweit limitiert und einzeln nummeriert.

Produktion beendet.

Limited Edition "Tender Love" 1998

Worldwide limited and numbered edition of 25,000 pcs.

Closed Edition.

Hum 2007
Katzenmama · Tender Love

Modell-Nr. Model No.	Größe / Size cm / inch	Modellierdatum Sculpting Date	
2008	11 / 4.25	1996	CE

Limitierte Ausgabe "Hundepapa" 1997

Auf 25.000 Stück weltweit limitiert und einzeln nummeriert.

Produktion beendet.

Limited Edition "Frisky Friends" 1997

Worldwide limited and numbered edition of 25,000 pcs.

Closed Edition.

Hum 2008
Hundepapa · Frisky Friends

Modell-Nr. Model No.	Größe / Size cm / inch	Modellierdatum Sculpting Date	
2012	17 / 6.75	1996	CE

Limitierte Ausgabe "Nikolaustag" 1997

Auf 20.000 Stück weltweit limitiert und einzeln nummeriert.

Produktion beendet.

Limited Edition "St. Nicolas Day" 1997

Worldwide limited and numbered edition of 20,000 pcs.

Closed Edition.

Hum 2012
Nikolaustag · St. Nicholas Day

2014/I

Modell-Nr. Model No.	Größe / Size cm / inch	Modellierdatum Sculpting Date	
2014/2/0	11 / 4.25	1996	OE
2014/I	14,5 / 5.75	1996	OE

Anmerkung/Note:

2014/2/0 Erste Ausgabe 2000 mit Sonderbodenbild im ersten Produktionsjahr.

First Issue 2000 with special backstamp in the first year of production.

2014/I Erste Ausgabe 1997 mit Sonderbodenbild im ersten Produktionsjahr.

First Issue 1997 with special backstamp in the first year of production.

Hum 2014
Aus der Bahn! · Christmas Delivery

OE: Offene Edition / Open Edition
CE: Produktion beendet / Closed Edition
TWD: Vorübergehend nicht mehr in Produktion / Temporarily withdrawn from production

Hum 2015
Am Weihnachtsbaum
Wonder Of Christmas

Modell-Nr. Model No.	Größe / Size cm / inch	Modellierdatum Sculpting Date	
2015	17,5 / 7.00	1996	OE seit / since 1999

Editionen mit Sonderbodenbild/ Editions with special backstamp:

Modell-Nr. Model No.	Ausgabejahr Year	Ausgabeort Country	
2015	1998	USA	CE

Sammler Set "Am Weihnachtsbaum"
Collectors Set "Wonder Of Christmas"

Sammler Set "Am Weihnachtsbaum" 1998

bestehend aus Hum 2015 und Teddybär der Firma Steiff.

Der Teddybär ist auf 20.000 Stück weltweit limitiert und einzeln nummeriert.

Erste Ausgabe 1998 mit Sonderbodenbild im ersten Produktionsjahr.

Produktion beendet.

Collector's Set "Wonder Of Christmas" 1998

consisting of Hum 2015 and Steiff Teddybaer.

The Teddy is a worldwide limited and numbered edition of 20,000 pcs.

First Issue 1998 with special backstamp in the first year of production.

Closed Edition.

Hum 2020
Stolzer Reitersmann · Riding Lesson

Modell-Nr. Model No.	Größe / Size cm / inch	Modellierdatum Sculpting Date	
2020	11,5 / 4.50	1996	OE

Anmerkung/Note:

Erste Ausgabe 2001 mit Sonderbodenbild im ersten Produktionsjahr.

First Issue 2001 with special backstamp in the first year of production.

OE: Offene Edition / Open Edition
CE: Produktion beendet / Closed Edition
TWD: Vorübergehend nicht mehr in Produktion / Temporarily withdrawn from production

Modell-Nr. Model No.	Größe / Size cm / inch	Modellierdatum Sculpting Date	
2021	10,5 / 4.25	1996	OE

Hum 2021
Kann schon reiten · Cowboy Coral

Anmerkung/Note:

Erste Ausgabe 2001 mit Sonderbodenbild im ersten Produktionsjahr.

First Issue 2001 with special backstamp in the first year of production.

Modell-Nr. Model No.	Größe / Size cm / inch	Modellierdatum Sculpting Date	
2025/A	17,5 / 6.75	1997	OE

Hum 2025/A
Gesucht, gefunden · Wishes Come True

Anmerkung/Note:

Exklusive Jahresedition für M.I.Hummel Clubmitglieder für das Clubjahr 2000/2001.

Exclusive Annual Edition for members of the M.I.Hummel Club in Club Year 2000/2001.

Erste Ausgabe innerhalb der Serie "Kindheitsträume".

First Issue in the "Wonder Of Childhood" series.

Modell-Nr. Model No.	Größe / Size cm / inch	Modellierdatum Sculpting Date	
2027	410 / 4.00	1996	OE

Hum 2027
Ostereiermalen · Easter's Coming

Anmerkung/Note:

Erste Ausgabe 2001 mit Sonderbodenbild im ersten Produktionsjahr.

First Issue 2001 with special backstamp in the first year of production.

OE: Offene Edition / Open Edition
CE: Produktion beendet / Closed Edition
TWD: Vorübergehend nicht mehr in Produktion / Temporarily withdrawn from production

Hum 2028
Aus dem Weg! · Winter Adventure

Modell-Nr. Model No.	Größe / Size cm / inch	Modellierdatum Sculpting Date	
2028	11 / 4.25	1996	OE ab 7/2001

Editionen mit Sonderbodenbild/ Editions with special backstamp:

Modell-Nr. Model No.	Ausgabejahr Year	Ausgabeland Country	
2028	2000	USA	OE

Anmerkung/Note:

Offene Edition ab 2001 mit Sonderbodenbild 2001 im ersten Produktionsjahr.

Open Edition 2001 with special backstamp 2001 in the first year of production.

Hum 2030
Wasser Marsch · Fire Fighter

Modell-Nr. Model No.	Größe / Size cm / inch	Modellierdatum Sculpting Date	
2030	11 / 4.25	1997	OE

Anmerkung/Note:

Erste Ausgabe 2000 mit Sonderbodenbild im ersten Produktionsjahr.

First Issue 2001 with special backstamp in the first year of production.

Hum 2031
Petri Heil · Catch Of The Day

Modell-Nr. Model No.	Größe / Size cm / inch	Modellierdatum Sculpting Date	
2031	11 / 4.25	1997	OE

Anmerkung/Note:

Erste Ausgabe 2000 mit Sonderbodenbild im ersten Produktionsjahr.

First Issue 2000 with special backstamp in the first year of production.

OE: Offene Edition / Open Edition
CE: Produktion beendet / Closed Edition
TWD: Vorübergehend nicht mehr in Produktion / Temporarily withdrawn from production

Hum 2032
Magst' probieren? · Puppy Pause

Modell-Nr. Model No.	Größe / Size cm / inch	Modellierdatum Sculpting Date	
2032	11 / 4.25	1997	OE ab 2002

Editionen mit Sonderbodenbild/ Editions with special backstamp:

Modell-Nr. Model No.	Ausgabejahr Year	Ausgabeland Country	
2032	2000	USA	OE
2032	2000	USA	OE

Anmerkung/Note:

Offene Edition ab 2002.

Open Edition 2002.

Hum 2035
Mei, ist die schwer · First Snow

Modell-Nr. Model No.	Größe / Size cm / inch	Modellierdatum Sculpting Date	
2035	14 / 5.50	1997	OE

Anmerkung/Note:

Offene Edition ab 2000.

Open Edition 2000.

Hum 2036
Hoffentlich schneit's bald wieder
Let It Snow

Modell-Nr. Model No.	Größe / Size cm / inch	Modellierdatum Sculpting Date	
2036	13 / 5.00	1997	OE

Anmerkung/Note:

Offene Edition ab 2000.

Open Edition 2000.

OE: Offene Edition / Open Edition
CE: Produktion beendet / Closed Edition
TWD: Vorübergehend nicht mehr in Produktion / Temporarily withdrawn from production

Sammler Set "Winterzauber" 1999

bestehend aus Hum 2035, Hum 2036 und Schneemann der Firma Steiff.

Der Schneemann ist auf 20.000 Stück weltweit limitiert und einzeln nummeriert. Erste Ausgabe 1999 mit Sonderbodenbild im ersten Produktionsjahr.

Produktion beendet.

Collector's Set "Frosty Friends" 1999

consisting of Hum 2035, Hum 2036 and Steiff Snowman.

The Snowman is a worldwide limited and numbered edition of 20,000 pcs. First Issue 1999 with special backstamp in the first year of production.

Closed Edition.

Sammler Set "Winterzauber"
Collectors Set "Frosty Friends"

Hum 2038
Meisterkoch · In The Kitchen

Modell-Nr. Model No.	Größe / Size cm / inch	Modellierdatum Sculpting Date	
2038	11,5 / 4.50	1997	OE

Editionen mit Sonderbodenbild/ Editions with special backstamp:

Modell-Nr. Model No.	Ausgabejahr Year	Ausgabeland Country	
2038	1999	QVC, USA	CE

Anmerkung/Note:

Erste Ausgabe 2000 mit Sonderbodenbild im ersten Produktionsjahr.

First Issue 2000 with special backstamp in the first year of production.

Hum 2039
Merk' Dir's! · Halt!

Modell-Nr. Model No.	Größe / Size cm / inch	Modellierdatum Sculpting Date	
2039	12 / 4.75	1997	OE

Anmerkung/Note:

Erste Ausgabe 2000 mit Sonderbodenbild im ersten Produktionsjahr.

First Issue 2000 with special backstamp in the first year of production.

OE: Offene Edition / Open Edition
CE: Produktion beendet / Closed Edition
TWD: Vorübergehend nicht mehr in Produktion / Temporarily withdrawn from production

Hum 2040
Maler Klecksel · One Coat Or Two?

Modell-Nr. Model No.	Größe / Size cm / inch	Modellierdatum Sculpting Date	
2040	11,5 / 4.50	1997	OE

Editionen mit Sonderbodenbild/ Editions with special backstamp:

Modell-Nr. Model No.	Ausgabejahr Year	Ausgabeland Country	
2040	2000	Deutschland, Germany	CE

Anmerkung/Note:

Erste Ausgabe 2000 mit Sonderbodenbild im ersten Produktionsjahr.

First Issue 2000 with special backstamp in the first year of production.

Hum 2044
Bitte zurücktreten · All Aboard

Modell-Nr. Model No.	Größe / Size cm / inch	Modellierdatum Sculpting Date	
2044	12,5 / 5.00	1997	OE

Anmerkung/Note:

Erste Ausgabe 2001 mit Sonderbodenbild im ersten Produktionsjahr.

First Issue 2001 with special backstamp in the first year of production.

Hum 2049/A
Mein Kuschelbär · Cuddles

Modell-Nr. Model No.	Größe / Size cm / inch	Modellierdatum Sculpting Date	
2049/A/0	8 / 3.25	1998	OE
2049/A	9 / 3.50	1997	OE

Anmerkung/Note:

2049/A/0 Ornament. Vorerst nur in USA erhältlich.

Ornament. Only available in the US.

2049/A Erste Ausgabe 1998 mit Sonderbodenbild im ersten Produktionsjahr.

First Issue 1998 with special backstamp in the first year of production.

OE: Offene Edition / Open Edition
CE: Produktion beendet / Closed Edition
TWD: Vorübergehend nicht mehr in Produktion / Temporarily withdrawn from production

Modell-Nr. Model No.	Größe / Size cm / inch	Modellierdatum Sculpting Date	
2049/B/0	8 / 3.25	1998	OE
2049/B	9 / 3.50	1997	OE

Anmerkung/Note:

2049/B/0 Ornament. Vorerst nur in USA erhältlich.

Ornament. Only available in the US.

2049/B Erste Ausgabe 1998 mit Sonderbodenbild im ersten Produktionsjahr.

First Issue 1998 with special backstamp in the first year of production.

Hum 2049/B
Mein kleiner Freund · My Best Friend

Modell-Nr. Model No.	Größe / Size cm / inch	Modellierdatum Sculpting Date	
2050/A	8,5 / 3.25	1997	OE

Editionen mit Sonderbodenbild/ Editions with special backstamp:

Modell-Nr. Model No.	Ausgabejahr Year	Ausgabeland Country	
2050/A	1999	"Hummel, Bumble Bee" USA	CE

Anmerkung/Note:

Erste Ausgabe 1999 mit Sonderbodenbild im ersten Produktionsjahr.

First Issue1999 with special backstamp in the first year of production.

Hum 2050/A
Hab' Dir geschrieben · Messages Of Love

Modell-Nr. Model No.	Größe / Size cm / inch	Modellierdatum Sculpting Date	
2050/B	9 / 3.50	1997	OE

Anmerkung/Note:

Erste Ausgabe 1999 mit Sonderbodenbild im ersten Produktionsjahr.

First Issue1999 with special backstamp in the first year of production.

OE: Offene Edition / Open Edition
CE: Produktion beendet / Closed Edition
TWD: Vorübergehend nicht mehr in Produktion / Temporarily withdrawn from production

Hum 2050/B
Magst mich auch? · Be Mine

Modell-Nr. Model No.	Größe / Size cm / inch	Modellierdatum Sculpting Date	
2051/A	9 / 3.50	1997	OE

Editionen mit Sonderbodenbild/ Editions with special backstamp:

Modell-Nr. Model No.	Ausgabejahr Year	Ausgabeland Country	
2051/A	1998	"Miller's Expo" USA	CE
2051/A	2000	Deutschland, Germany	CE

Anmerkung/Note:

Erste Ausgabe 1998 mit Sonderbodenbild im ersten Produktionsjahr.

First Issue1998 with special backstamp in the first year of production.

Hum 2051/A
Hör zu · Once Upon A Time

Modell-Nr. Model No.	Größe / Size cm / inch	Modellierdatum Sculpting Date	
2051/B	9 / 3.50	1997	OE

Anmerkung/Note:

Erste Ausgabe 1998 mit Sonderbodenbild im ersten Produktionsjahr.

First Issue1998 with special backstamp in the first year of production.

Hum 2051/B
Spielst' mit mir? · Let's Play

Modell-Nr. Model No.	Größe / Size cm / inch	Modellierdatum Sculpting Date	
2052	9 / 3.50	1997	CE

Anmerkung/Note:

Exklusive Verlängerungsfigur für M.I.Hummel Clubmitglieder für

das Clubjahr 1999/2000.

Exclusive Renewal Figurine for members of the M.I.Hummel Club

in Club Year 1999/2000.

Hum 2052
Mein Glücksschweinchen · Pigtails

OE: Offene Edition / Open Edition
CE: Produktion beendet / Closed Edition
TWD: Vorübergehend nicht mehr in Produktion / Temporarily withdrawn from production

Modell-Nr. Model No.	Größe / Size cm / inch	Modellierdatum Sculpting Date	
2053	9 / 3.50	1997	CE

Hum 2053
Laß Dich streicheln · Playful Pals

Limitierte Ausgabe "Laß Dich streicheln" 1998

Auf 25.000 Stück weltweit limitiert und einzeln nummeriert. Produktion beendet.

Limited Edition "Playful Pals" 1998

Worldwide limited and numbered edition of 25,000 pcs. Closed Edition.

Modell-Nr. Model No.	Größe / Size cm / inch	Modellierdatum Sculpting Date	
2058/A	8 / 3.25	1998	OE

Hum 2058/A
Hilfst Du mir auf? · Skating Lesson

Anmerkung/Note:

Erste Ausgabe 2000 mit Sonderbodenbild im ersten Produktionsjahr.

First Issue2000 with special backstamp in the first year of production.

Modell-Nr. Model No.	Größe / Size cm / inch	Modellierdatum Sculpting Date	
2058/B	7,5 / 3.00	1998	OE

Hum 2058/B
Aller Anfang ist schwer · Skate In Stride

Anmerkung/Note:

Erste Ausgabe 2000 mit Sonderbodenbild im ersten Produktionsjahr.

First Issue2000 with special backstamp in the first year of production.

OE: Offene Edition / Open Edition
CE: Produktion beendet / Closed Edition
TWD: Vorübergehend nicht mehr in Produktion / Temporarily withdrawn from production

Modell-Nr. Model No.	Größe / Size cm / inch	Modellierdatum Sculpting Date	
2066	11 / 4.25	1998	CE

Hum 2066
Trau Dich · Peaceful Offering

Limitierte Ausgabe "Trau Dich" 1999

Auf 25.000 Stück weltweit limitiert und einzeln nummeriert. Produktion beendet.

Limited Edition "Peaceful Offering" 1999

Worldwide limited and numbered edition of 25,000 pcs. Closed Edition.

Modell-Nr. Model No.	Größe / Size cm / inch	Modellierdatum Sculpting Date	
2067/A/0	8 / 3.25	1998	OE
2067/A	8,5 / 3.25	1998	OE

Hum 2067/A
Hab' was Gutes · Sweet Treats

Anmerkung/Note:

2067/A/0 Ornament. Vorerst nur in USA erhältlich.

Ornament. Only available in the US.

2067/A Erste Ausgabe 2000 mit Sonderbodenbild im ersten Produktionsjahr.

First Issue 2000 with special backstamp in the first year of production.

Modell-Nr. Model No.	Größe / Size cm / inch	Modellierdatum Sculpting Date	
2067/B/0	8 / 3.25	1998	OE
2067/B	9 / 3.50	1998	OE

Anmerkung/Note:

2067/B/0 Ornament. Vorerst nur in USA erhältlich.

Ornament. Only available in the US.

2067/B Erste Ausgabe 2000 mit Sonderbodenbild im ersten Produktionsjahr.

First Issue 2000 with special backstamp in the first year of production.

Hum 2067/B
Nur 'ne Kleinigkeit · For Me?

OE: Offene Edition / Open Edition
CE: Produktion beendet / Closed Edition
TWD: Vorübergehend nicht mehr in Produktion / Temporarily withdrawn from production

Modell-Nr. Model No.	Größe / Size cm / inch	Modellierdatum Sculpting Date	
2071	9 / 3.50	1998	CE

Hum 2071
Glücksbote · Lucky Charmer

Anmerkung/Note:

Exklusive Jahresedition für M.I.Hummel Clubmitglieder für das Clubjahr 1999/2000.

Exclusive Annual Edition for members of the M.I.Hummel Club in Club Year 1999/2000.

Modell-Nr. Model No.	Größe / Size cm / inch	Modellierdatum Sculpting Date	
2073/A	10 / 4.00	1999	OE

Hum 2073/A
Kling Glöckchen kling
Ring In The Season

Anmerkung/Note:

Erste Ausgabe 2001 mit Sonderbodenbild im ersten Produktionsjahr.

First Issue 2001 with special backstamp in the first year of production.

Modell-Nr. Model No.	Größe / Size cm / inch	Modellierdatum Sculpting Date	
2073/B	10 / 4.00	1999	OE

Hum 2073/B
...den schenk ich Dir · Christmas Carol

Anmerkung/Note:

Erste Ausgabe 2001 mit Sonderbodenbild im ersten Produktionsjahr.

First Issue 2001 with special backstamp in the first year of production.

OE: Offene Edition / Open Edition
CE: Produktion beendet / Closed Edition
TWD: Vorübergehend nicht mehr in Produktion / Temporarily withdrawn from production

Modell-Nr. Model No.	Größe / Size cm / inch	Modellierdatum Sculpting Date	
2074/A/0	8 / 3.25	1998	OE
2074/A	9 / 3.50	1998	OE

Editionen mit Sonderbodenbild/ Editions with special backstamp:

Modell-Nr. Model No.	Ausgabejahr Year	Ausgabeland Country	
2074/A	1999	Deutschland, Germany	CE

Anmerkung/Note:

2074/A/0 Ornament. Vorerst nur in USA erhältlich.

Ornament. Only available in the US.

2074/A Erste Ausgabe 1998 mit Sonderbodenbild im ersten Produktionsjahr.

First Issue 1998 with special backstamp in the first year of production.

Hum 2074/A
Mein Maskottchen · Christmas Gift

Modell-Nr. Model No.	Größe / Size cm / inch	Modellierdatum Sculpting Date	
2075	11 / 4.25	1998	OE

Anmerkung/Note:

Erste Ausgabe 2000 mit Sonderbodenbild im ersten Produktionsjahr.

First Issue 2000 with special backstamp in the first year of production.

Hum 2075
Erste Hilfe · Comfort And Care

Modell-Nr. Model No.	Größe / Size cm / inch	Modellierdatum Sculpting Date	
2077/A	8 / 3.00	1998	OE
2077/A/0	7,5 / 3.00	1998	OE

Anmerkung/Note:

2077/A/0 Ornament. Vorerst nur in USA erhältlich.

Ornament. Only available in the US.

2077/A Erste Ausgabe 2000 mit Sonderbodenbild im ersten Produktionsjahr.

First Issue 2000 with special backstamp in the first year of production.

Hum 2077/A
Drob'n auf'n Berg war i · First Bloom

OE: Offene Edition / Open Edition
CE: Produktion beendet / Closed Edition
TWD: Vorübergehend nicht mehr in Produktion / Temporarily withdrawn from production

Hum 2077/B
Für Dich gepflückt · A Flower For You

Modell-Nr. Model No.	Größe / Size cm / inch	Modellierdatum Sculpting Date	
2077/B	8 / 3.00	1998	OE
2077/B/0	7,5 / 3.00	1998	OE

Anmerkung/Note:

2077/B/0 Ornament. Vorerst nur in USA erhältlich.

Ornament. Only available in the US.

2077/B Erste Ausgabe 2000 mit Sonderbodenbild im ersten Produktionsjahr.

First Issue 2000 with special backstamp in the first year of production.

Hum 2085
Ich helf' dem Opa · Little Farm Hand

Modell-Nr. Model No.	Größe / Size cm / inch	Modellierdatum Sculpting Date	
2085	12 / 4.75	1998	CE

Limitierte Ausgabe "Ich helf' dem Opa" 1999

Auf 25.000 Stück weltweit limitiert und einzeln nummeriert. Produktion beendet.

Limited Edition "Little Farm Hand" 1999

Worldwide limited and numbered edition of 25,000 pcs. Closed Edition.

Hum 2086
Ich helf' der Oma · Spring Sowing

Modell-Nr. Model No.	Größe / Size cm / inch	Modellierdatum Sculpting Date	
2086	9 / 3.50	1998	OE

Limitierte Ausgabe "Ich helf' der Oma" 2000

Auf 25.000 Stück weltweit limitiert und einzeln nummeriert.

Limited Edition "Spring Sowing" 2000

Worldwide limited and numbered edition of 25,000 pcs.

OE: Offene Edition / Open Edition
CE: Produktion beendet / Closed Edition
TWD: Vorübergehend nicht mehr in Produktion / Temporarily withdrawn from production

Modell-Nr. Model No.	Größe / Size cm / inch	Modellierdatum Sculpting Date	
2087/A	9,5 / 4.00	1999	OE bis Mai 2001 until May 2001

Anmerkung/Note:

Exklusive Jahresedition für M.I.Hummel Clubmitglieder für das Clubjahr 2000/2001.

Exclusive Annual Edition for members of the M.I.Hummel Club in Club Year 2000/2001.

Hum 2087/A
Kann schon schreiben · Sharpest Student

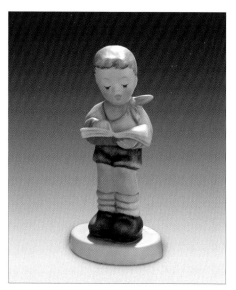

Modell-Nr. Model No.	Größe / Size cm / inch	Modellierdatum Sculpting Date	
2087	9,5 / 3.75	1999	OE bis Mai 2001 until May 2001

Anmerkung/Note:

Exklusive Verlängerungsfigur für M.I.Hummel Clubmitglieder für das Clubjahr 2000/2001.

Exclusive Renewal Figurine for members of the M.I.Hummel Club in Club Year 2000/2001.

Hum 2087/B
ABC-Stunde · Honor Student

Modell-Nr. Model No.	Größe / Size cm / inch	Modellierdatum Sculpting Date	
2091	10,5 / 4.00	1999	OE

Anmerkung/Note:

Erste Ausgabe 2001 mit Sonderbodenbild im ersten Produktionsjahr.

First Issue 2001 with special backstamp in the first year of production.

Hum 2091
Bitte schön · Maid To Order

OE: Offene Edition / Open Edition
CE: Produktion beendet / Closed Edition
TWD: Vorübergehend nicht mehr in Produktion / Temporarily withdrawn from production

Modell-Nr. Model No.	Größe / Size cm / inch	Modellierdatum Sculpting Date	
2092	11 / 4.25	1999	OE

Anmerkung/Note:

Erste Ausgabe 2001 mit Sonderbodenbild im ersten Produktionsjahr.

First Issue 2001 with special backstamp in the first year of production.

Hum 2092
Schnipp-Schnapp · Make Me Pretty

Modell-Nr. Model No.	Größe / Size cm / inch	Modellierdatum Sculpting Date	
2093	10,5 / 4.25	1998	OE

Editionen mit Sonderbodenbild/ Editions with special backstamp:

Modell-Nr. Model No.	Ausgabejahr Year	Ausgabeland Country	
2093	2000	"M.I.Hummel Club Convention" Deutschland, Germany	CE

Anmerkung/Note:

Erste Ausgabe 2000 mit Sonderbodenbild im ersten Produktionsjahr.

First Issue 2000 with special backstamp in the first year of production.

Hum 2093
Frisch gezapft · Pretzel Boy

Modell-Nr. Model No.	Größe / Size cm / inch	Modellierdatum Sculpting Date	
2094	10 / 4.00	1999	TWD

Editionen mit Sonderbodenbild/ Editions with special backstamp:

Modell-Nr. Model No.	Ausgabejahr Year	Ausgabeort Country	
2094	1999	QVC, USA	CE

Hum 2094
Ich mach' Licht · Christmas Wish

OE: Offene Edition / Open Edition
CE: Produktion beendet / Closed Edition
TWD: Vorübergehend nicht mehr in Produktion / Temporarily withdrawn from production

Hum 2096/H
Engel mit Bandoneon · Millennium Bliss

	Modell-Nr. Model No.	Größe / Size cm / inch	Modellierdatum Sculpting Date		
①	2096/A	10,5 / 4.25	1999	Dirigentenengel Angelic Conductor	OE
②	2096/C	10,5 / 4.25	1999	Engel mit Trommel Celestial Drummer	OE
③	2096/E	10 / 4.00	1999	Flötenengel Heavenly Rhapsodie	OE
④	2096/F	10 / 4.00	1999	Geigenengel Celestial Strings	OE
⑤	2096/J	10 / 4.00	1999	Engel mit Horn Heavenly Horn Player	OE
	2096/H	11,5 / 4.50	1999	Engel mit Bandoneon Millennium Bliss	CE
	2096/K	11,5 / 4.50	1999	Engel mit Panflöte Joyful Recital	OE

Hum 2096/K
Engel mit Panflöte · Joyful Recital

Anmerkung/Note:

2096/A, C, E, F, J Erste Ausgabe 2000 mit Sonderbodenbild im ersten Produktionsjahr.
First Issue 2000 with special backstamp in the first year of production.

2096/H Jahresengel 2000.
Annual Angel 2000.

2096/K Jahresengel 2001.
Annual Angel 2001.

OE: Offene Edition / Open Edition
CE: Produktion beendet / Closed Edition
TWD: Vorübergehend nicht mehr in Produktion / Temporarily withdrawn from production

Modell-Nr. Model No.	Größe / Size cm / inch	Modellierdatum Sculpting Date	
2098/A	9 / 3.50	1999	CE
2098/B	9 / 3.50	1999	OE

2098/B

Anmerkung/Note:

2098/A Jahres Christbaumschmuck Stern 2000.

Annual Christmas Tree Ornament Star 2000.

2098/B Jahres Christbaumschmuck Stern 2001.

Annual Christmas Tree Ornament Star 2001.

2098/A

Hum 2098/A
Engel mit Bandoneon · Millennium Bliss

Modell-Nr. Model No.	Größe / Size cm / inch	Modellierdatum Sculpting Date	
2099/A	8,5 / 3.25	1999	OE

Anmerkung/Note:

Christbaumschmuck Stiefel. Erste Ausgabe 2000.

Christmas Tree Ornament Boot. First Issue 2000.

Hum 2099/A
Nikolaustag · St. Nicholas Day

Modell-Nr. Model No.	Größe / Size cm / inch	Modellierdatum Sculpting Date	
2101/A	10 / 4.00	1999	OE

Anmerkung/Note:

Erste Ausgabe 2001 mit Sonderbodenbild im ersten Produktionsjahr.

First Issue 2001 with special backstamp in the first year of production.

Hum 2101/A
Mein kleiner Schatz · A Girl's Best Friend

Modell-Nr. Model No.	Größe / Size cm / inch	Modellierdatum Sculpting Date	
2101/B	10 / 4.00	1999	OE

Anmerkung/Note:

Erste Ausgabe 2001 mit Sonderbodenbild im ersten Produktionsjahr.

First Issue 2001 with special backstamp in the first year of production.

Hum 2101/B
Für immer Freunde · A Boy's Best Friend

Modell-Nr. Model No.	Größe / Size cm / inch	Modellierdatum Sculpting Date	
2104	9 / 3.50	1999	OE

Anmerkung/Note:

Treuefigur für Mitglieder des M.I.Hummel Club, die in ihrem fünften, persönlichen Mitgliedsjahr sind.

Loyalty figurine for members of the M.I.Hummel Club in their 5th personal membership year.

Hum 2104
Süße kleine Hummel · Sunflower Friends

Modell-Nr. Model No.	Größe / Size cm / inch	Modellierdatum Sculpting Date	
2105	7 / 2.75	1999	OE

Anmerkung/Note:

Treuefigur für Mitglieder des M.I.Hummel Club, die in ihrem zehnten, persönlichen Mitgliedsjahr sind.

Loyalty figurine for members of the M.I.Hummel Club in their 10th personal membership year.

Hum 2105
Summ, Summ... · Miss Beehaving

OE: Offene Edition / Open Edition
CE: Produktion beendet / Closed Edition
TWD: Vorübergehend nicht mehr in Produktion / Temporarily withdrawn from production

Modell-Nr. Model No.	Größe / Size cm / inch	Modellierdatum Sculpting Date	
2107/A	10,5 / 4.00	1999	OE

Limitierte Ausgabe "Hab's von Oma gelernt" 2000

Auf 25.000 Stück weltweit limitiert und einzeln nummeriert.

Limited Edition "Bee Hopeful" 2000

Worldwide limited and numbered edition of 25,000 pcs.

Hum 2107/A
Hab's von Oma gelernt · Bee Hopeful

Modell-Nr. Model No.	Größe / Size cm / inch	Modellierdatum Sculpting Date	
2107/B	10,5 / 4.00	1999	OE ab / from 5 / 2001

Limitierte Ausgabe "Ich helf der Schwester" 2001

Auf 25.000 Stück weltweit limitiert und einzeln nummeriert.

Limited Edition "Little Knitter" 2001

Worldwide limited and numbered edition of 25,000 pcs.

Hum 2107/B
Ich helf der Schwester · Little Knitter

Modell-Nr. Model No.	Größe / Size cm / inch	Modellierdatum Sculpting Date	
2110/A	9 / 3.50	1999	OE

Anmerkung/Note:

Christbaumschmuck Stern. Erste Ausgabe 1999.

Christmas Tree Ornament Star. First Issue 1999.

Hum 2110/A
Aus der Bahn · Christmas Delivery

OE: Offene Edition / Open Edition
CE: Produktion beendet / Closed Edition
TWD: Vorübergehend nicht mehr in Produktion / Temporarily withdrawn from production

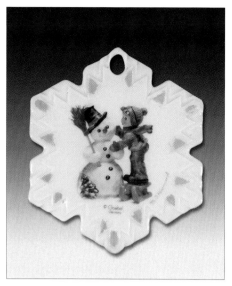

Modell-Nr. Model No.	Größe / Size cm / inch	Modellierdatum Sculpting Date	
2111/A	9 / 3.50	1999	OE

Anmerkung/Note:

Christbaumschmuck Schneekristall. Erste Ausgabe 1999.

Christmas Tree Ornament Snow Flake. First Issue 1999.

Hum 2111/A
Winterfreunde · Making New Friends

Modell-Nr. Model No.	Größe / Size cm / inch	Modellierdatum Sculpting Date	
2116/A	9,5 / 3.75	2000	OE

Anmerkung/Note:

Erste Ausgabe 2001 mit Sonderbodenbild im ersten Produktionsjahr.

First Issue 2001 with special backstamp in the first year of production.

Hum 2116/A
Fehlt noch was? · One Cup Of Sugar

Modell-Nr. Model No.	Größe / Size cm / inch	Modellierdatum Sculpting Date	
2116/B	10 / 4.00	2000	OE

Anmerkung/Note:

Erste Ausgabe 2001 mit Sonderbodenbild im ersten Produktionsjahr.

First Issue 2001 with special backstamp in the first year of production.

Hum 2116/B
Backe backe Kuchen · Baking Time

OE: Offene Edition / Open Edition
CE: Produktion beendet / Closed Edition
TWD: Vorübergehend nicht mehr in Produktion / Temporarily withdrawn from production

Miniaturen
Miniatures

OE
Wanderbub /Merry Wanderer
2,2 cm, 0.75 inch

OE
Puppenbad /Doll Bath
2,2 cm, 0.75 inch

OE
Geigerlein /Little Fiddler
2,2 cm, 0.75 inch

TWD
Kehrliesl /Little Sweeper
2,2 cm, 0.75 inch

OE
Krankenbesuch
Visiting An Invalid
2,2 cm, 0.75 inch

OE
Herbst /Apple Tree Boy
2,2 cm, 0.75 inch

TWD
Unter einem Dach
Stormy Weather
2,2 cm, 0.75 inch

OE
Eilbote/Postman
2,2 cm, 0.75 inch

OE
Aschenputtel /Cinderella
2,2 cm, 0.75 inch

OE
Ständchen /Serenade
2,2 cm, 0.75 inch

OE
Herr Ober /Waiter
2,2 cm, 0.75 inch

OE
Der kleine Konditor /Baker
2,2 cm, 0.75 inch

OE
Musterschülerin
Busy Student
2,2 cm, 0.75 inch

TWD
Schulschwänzer/School Boy
2,2 cm, 0.75 inch

OE
Bandoneonspieler
Accordion Boy
2,2 cm, 0.75 inch

OE
Wir gratulieren
We Congratulate
2,2 cm, 0.75 inch

TWD
Vaters G'scheitester
Wayside Harmony
2,2 cm, 0.75 inch

TWD
Gänseliesl /Goose Girl
2,2 cm, 0.75 inch

TWD
Händlerschild, englisch/Dealer
Plaque, English
1,8 cm, 0.50 inch

OE
Händlerschild, deutsch/Dealer
Plaque, German
1,8 cm, 0.50 inch

OE
Der kleine Konditor · Herr Ober/
In der Bäckerei
Baker · Waiter/Bakery Day
12 cm, 4.75 inch

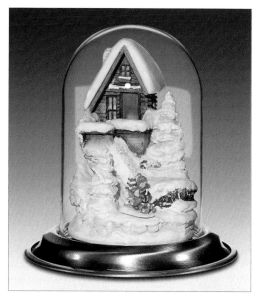

TWD
Fahrt in die Weihnacht, Einzelfigur
Ride Into Christmas, Single Figurine
2,2 cm, 0.75 inch

TWD
Fahrt in die Weihnacht/ Winterfest
Ride Into Christmas/ Winterfest
12 cm, 4.75 inch

OE
Trara, die Post ist da/ Glockenturm
The Mail Is Here/Clock Tower
19 cm, 7.50 inch

OE
Trara, die Post ist da, Einzelfigur
The Mail Is Here, Single Figurine
2,2 cm, 0.75 inch

TWD
Wir gratulieren/Bayerischer Blumenstand
We Congratulate/Bavarian Flower Stand
12 cm, 4.75 inch

CE
Ringelreihen, Tanz um den
Maibaum
Limitiert auf 10.000 Stück
Ring Around The Rosie
Musical Vignette
Limited Edition of 10,000 pcs.
19 cm, 7.50 inch

OE
Ringelreihen, Einzelfigur
Ring Around The Rosie, Single Figurine
6 cm, 2.50 inch

TWD
Bandoneonspieler,
Bayerisches Haus
Accordion Boy,
Bavarian House
12 cm, 4.75 inch

TWD
Schäferbub
Lost Sheep
40 cm, 15.75 inch

TWD
Eilbote
Postman
40 cm, 15.75 inch

TWD
Frühlingsidyll
Signs Of Spring
40 cm, 15.75 inch

TWD
Geburtstagsständchen (Junge)
Birthday Serenade (Boy)
40 cm, 15.75 inch

TWD
Geburtstagsständchen (Mädchen)
Birthday Serenade (Girl)
40 cm, 15.75 inch

TWD
Fastnacht
Carnival
40 cm, 15.75 inch

TWD
Zum Festtag
On Holiday
40 cm, 15.75 inch

TWD
Ostergruß
Easter Greetings
40 cm, 15.75 inch

TWD: Vorübergehend nicht mehr in Produktion
Temporarily withdrawn from production

Puppen-Information

Im Jahre 1950 begann die Produktion von Spielwaren und Puppen. Zu diesem Zeitpunkt wurden die Puppen aus zwei verschiedenen Materialien hergestellt,

– komplett aus Gummi
– oder mit ausgestopftem Weichkörper und Kopf aus Gummi

Der Gummi der allerersten M.I.Hummel-Puppenköpfe war „Hartgummi", der leicht mit Papiermaché oder sogar Porzellan verwechselt werden kann. Später wurde dann der sogenannte „Weichgummi" verwendet. Anfang der sechziger Jahre ging man dazu über, die Fabrikation von Gummi auf PVC/Vinyl, einem sehr dauerhaften Material, umzustellen.

Die **ersten 7 M.I.Hummel-Puppen**, die 1950 hergestellt wurden,

Hum 1	„Gretl"		Hum 5	„Strickliesl"
Hum 2	„Seppl"		Hum 6	„Max"
Hum 3	„Bertl"		Hum 7	„Wanderbub"
Hum 4	„Hansl"			

gab es in zwei verschiedenen Größen:

– in ca. 42 cm (Serien 500 + 1500) und in ca. 28 cm (Serie 1600)

und in zwei verschiedenen Ausführungen:

– zuerst als weich gestopfte Gelenkpuppe mit Gummikopf (Serie 500)
– ein Jahr später dann als Gummi-Gelenkpuppe: Haare modelliert - Kopf, Arme und Beine beweglich (Serien 1500 und 1600)

Die gestopften Puppen mit Gummikopf wurden nur ca. 2 Jahre hergestellt, anfangs von der Firma Hermann Steiner in Neustadt bei Coburg. Das Anziehen erfolgte bei Goebel. Die Kleidung der Puppen wurde in einem eigenen Atelier von versierten Designerinnen und Näherinnen entworfen und genäht. Ab 1952 wurden auch die Puppenkörper von Goebel produziert, und zwar aus Gummi.

Im Laufe der Jahre kamen aufgrund der großen Nachfrage die nachfolgenden Serien auf den Markt:

500	ca. 42 cm		1950	weich gestopfte Gelenkpuppe mit Gummikopf
1101	ca. 33 cm	beginnend	1953	Babies, handbemalte Augen, aus Gummi
1102	ca. 26 cm	beginnend	1954	Babies, handbemalte Augen, aus Gummi
1500	ca. 42 cm		1951	Gummi-Gelenkpuppe, Haare modelliert
1600	ca. 28 cm		1951	Gummi-Gelenkpuppe, Haare modelliert
1700	ca. 28 cm	beginnend	1954/55	anfangs aus Gummi, später aus Vinyl
1809 - 1812	ca. 35 cm	beginnend	1954/55	anfangs aus Gummi, später aus Vinyl
1801 - 1806	ca. 20 cm	beginnend ca.	1967/68	aus Vinyl
1960	ca. 39 cm	beginnend	1958	aus Gummi, vollbeweglich, Knüpfhaar, gemalte Augen
1961	ca. 35 cm	beginnend	1958/59	aus Gummi und Vinyl, vollbeweglich, mit eingeknüpftem Kunsthaar und Glasaugen
2961	ca. 35 cm	beginnend	1964	aus PVC, vollbeweglich, mit eingeknüpftem Kunsthaar und Schlafaugen
V 103	ca. 33 cm		1960	aus PVC, vollbeweglich, Haar modelliert, mit Glasaugen
V 104	ca. 26 cm		1960	aus PVC, vollbeweglich, Haar modelliert, mit Glasaugen
V 203	ca. 33 cm		1964	aus PVC, vollbeweglich, Haar modelliert, mit Schlafaugen
V 204	ca. 26 cm		1964	aus PVC, vollbeweglich, Haar modelliert, mit Schlafaugen
V 105	ca. 33 cm		1962	aus PVC, vollbeweglich, Haar eingeknüpft, Glasaugen
V 205	ca. 33 cm		1964	aus PVC, vollbeweglich, Haar eingeknüpft, Schlafaugen

Die Puppe mit der Modell-Nummer **1961** hatte eingeknüpftes Haar und Glasaugen. Sie war mit mehreren verschiedenen Kleiderausstattungen erhältlich.

Die Puppe **2961** ist die gleiche Puppe wie 1961 jedoch mit Schlafaugen (geschaffen 1964).

Im Jahr 1953 erblickte das M.I.Hummel-Baby das Licht der Puppenwelt. Das Baby gab es in zwei Größen: Serie 1101 ca. 33 cm, Serie 1102 ca. 26 cm Es war erhältlich mit vielen verschiedenen Ausstattungen. Zu Beginn waren die Augen handgemalt. Ab 1960 wurden die Babies auch mit Glas- **(V 103, V 104 und V 105)** und ab 1964 mit Schlafaugen **(V 203, V 204 und V 205)** gemacht.

Modelleur all dieser Hummel-Puppen war Karl Wagner. Bei ihm in die Lehre ging Helmut Fischer, der 1982 die M.I.Hummel-Porzellanpuppen schuf.

Im Jahre 1975 wurde die Spielwarenfabrikation bis auf einige M.I.Hummel-Puppen-Modelle aus Vinyl eingestellt. Diese Vinyl-Puppen wurden 1983/84 von einer Serie von M.I.Hummel-Porzellan-Puppen abgelöst.

Die nachfolgenden 7 Hummel-Puppen aus Porzellan wurden zwischen 1988 und 1994 exklusiv für die Firma Danbury Mint in USA hergestellt:

Hum 512	„Geborgen, Mädchen"	ab 1988
Hum 513	„Geigerlein"	ab 1988
Hum 514	„Die Heuschrecke"	ab 1989
Hum 516	„Wanderbub"	ab 1990
Hum 517	„Gänseliesl"	ab 1990
Hum 518	„Geborgen, Junge"	ab 1989
Hum 519	„Fahrt in die Weihnacht"	ab 1989

Bei jeder Hummel-Puppe sollte am Hals/Rücken die Signatur M.I.Hummel, die Fabrikmarke und die Seriennummer eingraviert sein. Leider kann man das Alter nicht genau bestimmen, da die Fabrikmarke in der Gußform aus Metall eingraviert war und die Gußformen bei Fabrikmarken-Änderungen nicht gleich geändert werden konnten.

Hier noch ein Hinweis zur Pflege von Gummi-Puppen:
In den ersten Fertigungsjahren wurden unsere Puppen aus Gummi hergestellt. Trotz aller technischen Erkenntnisse war und ist es nicht möglich, ein Altern des Gummis auszuschließen. Später gingen wir dann dazu über, unsere Spielwarenerzeugnisse aus PVC (Vinyl) zu fertigen, einem Material, das diesem Alterungsprozeß nicht unterliegt.

Hinauszögern kann man den Zerfall des Puppenkörpers unter Umständen wie folgt:
Puppenkörper und -kopf mit Zeitungspapier oder Watte hart ausstopfen. Kopf und Körper regelmäßig mit Vaseline oder einer anderen Fettcreme einfetten.

Doll Information

In 1950 Goebel started with the production of toys and dolls. At that time the dolls were made of two different materials, namely:
– completely of rubber
– or with a body of soft stuffed material and a rubber head.

The rubber, which was used for the heads of the very first *M.I.Hummel* dolls, was „hard rubber", which can easily be mistaken for papier-mâché or even porcelain. Later, so-called "soft rubber" was used. In the early sixties Goebel began to manufacture the dolls in vinyl, which is a very durable material.

The **first 7 *M.I.Hummel* dolls**, which were made in 1950,

Hum 1 "Sister"	Hum 5 "Happy Pastime"
Hum 2 "Brother"	Hum 6 "Our Hero"
Hum 3 "Little Shopper"	Hum 7 "Merry Wanderer"
Hum 4 "Little Hiker"	

were produced in two different sizes:

– in abt. 42 cm (Series 500 + 1500) and in abt. 28 cm (Series 1600)

and in two different executions:

– first as jointed dolls with soft-stuffed body and rubber head (Series 500)
– one year later, as jointed dolls made of rubber with modelled hair and moveable head, arms and legs (Series 1500 and 1600).

The soft-stuffed dolls with rubber heads were made for two years only, in the beginning by the firm of Hermann Steiner in Neustadt bei Coburg. At Goebel they were completed with the clothing. The dresses for the dolls were developed and sewn by experienced designers and seamstresses in Goebel's own studio. From 1952, Goebel also produced the rubber doll bodies.

In the course of the years, because of the great demand, the following series were put on the market:

500	abt. 42 cm		1950	soft-stuffed jointed doll with rubber head
1101	abt. 33 cm	beginning	1953	Babies, hand painted eyes, made of rubber
1102	abt. 26 cm	beginning	1954	Babies, hand painted eyes, made of rubber
1500	abt. 42 cm		1951	jointed rubber doll with modelled hair
1600	abt. 28 cm		1951	jointed rubber doll with modelled hair
1700	abt. 28 cm	beginning	1954/55	in the beginning made of rubber, later of vinyl
1809 - 1812	abt. 35 cm	beginning	1954/55	in the beginning made of rubber, later of vinyl
1801 - 1806	abt. 20 cm	beginning	1967/68	made of vinyl
1960	abt. 39 cm	beginning	1958	of rubber, completely moveable, hair sewn in, painted eyes
1961	abt. 35 cm	beginning	1958/59	of rubber and vinyl, completely moveable, hair sewn in and glass eyes
2961	abt. 35 cm	beginning	1964	of PVC, completely moveable, with hair sewn in and „sleeping" eyes
V 103	abt. 33 cm		1960	of PVC, completely moveable, modelled hair and glass eyes
V 104	abt 26 cm		1960	of PVC, completely moveable, modelled hair and glass eyes
V 203	abt. 33 cm		1964	of PVC, completely moveable, modelled hair and „sleeping" eyes
V 204	abt. 26 cm		1964	of PVC, completely moveable, modelled hair and „sleeping" eyes
V 105	abt. 33 cm		1962	of PVC, completely moveable, hair sewn in and glass eyes
V 205	abt. 33 cm		1964	of PVC, completely moveable, hair sewn in and „sleeping" eyes

The doll with the model number **1961** had sewn-in hair and glass eyes. She was available with several different dresses.

The doll **2961** is the same doll as 1961, however, with „sleeping" eyes (created in 1964).

In the 1953 *M.I.Hummel* baby was born. The baby was made in two different sizes: series 1101 abt. 33 cm and series 1102 abt. 26 cm. It was available with many different garments. At the beginning the eyes were hand painted. From 1960 the babies were also made with glass eyes **(V 103, V 104 and V 105)** and from 1964 with „sleeping" eyes **(V 203, V 204 and V 205)**.

Sculptor of all these Hummel dolls was Karl Wagner. He trained Helmut Fischer, who sculpted the M.I.Hummel porcelain dolls in 1982.

In 1975 the toy production was ended, except for some *M.I.Hummel* doll models made of vinyl. The vinyl dolls were replaced in 1983/84 by a series of *M.I.Hummel* porcelain dolls.

The following 7 Hummel dolls made of porcelain were exclusively produced by Goebel between 1988 and 1994 for the company Danbury Mint in the USA:

Hum 512	"Umbrella Girl"	as of 1988
Hum 513	"Little Fiddler"	as of 1988
Hum 514	"Friend or Foe?"	as of 1989
Hum 516	"Merry Wanderer"	as of 1990
Hum 517	"Goose Girl"	as of 1990
Hum 518	"Umbrella Boy"	as of 1989
Hum 519	"Ride into Christmas"	as of 1989

On each Hummel doll, at the back of the neck or the back, the signature M.I.Hummel, the trademark and the series number has to be engraved. Unfortunately, he exact age of the dolls cannot be determined, as the trademark was engraved in the metal chill mould and the chill moulds could not immediately be changed when the trademark was changed.

Here are some hints how to preserve any rubber dolls:
In the first years of production our dolls were made of rubber. Despite all technical knowledge it wasn't and isn't possible to prevent rubber from aging. Later on, we started to use PVC (vinyl) for the production of our toys. It is a material that doesn't suffer form this aging process.

Sometimes you can prevent further deterioration by filling the doll's body and head with newspaper or cotton wool. Head and body should be rubbed in regularly with vaseline or another rich oil-based cream.

Index

Index

Index

Index

Index

Index

Index

270

Index